**Institute of Public
and
Environmental Health**

THE UNIVE␣␣ Y
OF BIRMIN␣ ␣AM

west mid␣␣␣ds
HEALT␣␣␣

**Birmingham
City Council**

Resource Allocation &

Health Needs:

from Research to Policy

Proceedings of a conference held to consider assessment of health care needs in relation to framing policies for allocating resources in the Health Service

Introduced by:
Professor Rod Griffiths

Keynote speakers:
Professor Brian Jarman
Dr Vera Carstairs
Dr Bobbie Jacobson

Edited by:
Dr Estelle Gilman
Dr Stephen Munday
Dr Lillian Somervaille
Dr Rachel Strachan

London HMSO

Institute of Public and Environmental Health
The University of Birmingham
The Medical School
Edgbaston
Birmingham
B15 2TT

First published 1994

ISBN 0 11 701774 4

Contents

iv

Preface

Can policies for allocating resources in the Health Service be equitable and include assessment of the health needs of different populations? This is a topic on which there is currently vigorous debate. In particular differing views are expressed on the value of using various measures, such as deprivation or mortality rates, as indicators of health care needs. The data emerging from the 1991 census has provided further impetus to review the basis on which resources are allocated, both from the Department of Health to the Regional Health Authorities and from the regions to the District Health Authorities.

To widen the debate this national conference was organised by the Institute of Public and Environmental Health with the following objectives:

- to review the research on assessment of health care needs and their value in this field

- to address how these findings may contribute in the framing and implementation of policies for resource allocation in the health service

The Institute of Public and Environmental Health is a joint venture between The University of Birmingham, West Midlands Health and Birmingham City Council

Introduction to the Resource Allocation Debate

ROD K GRIFFITHS, Director, Institute of Public & Environmental Health, University of Birmingham

This paper will give a brief overview of resource allocation and the assessment of need and an introduction to the conference.

Since the introduction of the RAWP formula it has been clear that there is a dilemma in resource allocation between paying for service levels established by historical factors and driving policy intentions for the future. There is further debate about what those policy aims should be. The pursuit of equity is clearly on everyone's agenda but equality of outcome might cost different amounts in different places. Hence there is debate about whether such things as rural deprivation exist or whether providing care in rural areas costs more for a given outcome and hence should be resourced differently. It is also clear that patterns of illness vary in different social and ethnic groups and might therefore have different cost imperatives.

It is also unclear how much of the problem should be tackled at different levels in the system. Regions are sufficiently large that a broad brush might do. Allocation between districts and FHSAs (merged or not) could be left to RHAs, but what if they all pursue very different policies? As districts are merged some of the big differences may be averaged out. Should there be allocation policies inside districts? How small a unit can we go down to? This question has been given added spice by the intrusion of Fundholders on the scene. It is now clear that we must find a way of allocating to fundholders on a basis that is equitable and also fits with that used for DHAs. The problems of historic use versus policy direction loom even larger at the level of the fundholder where the variations in historic use of some services vary by many more times than they ever did between districts.

Implementation issues

Changing resource allocation formulae brings a different set of problems, most of which were seen with RAWP, but which are inherent in any change. New resources given to an authority that has not had them before may outstrip the capital base or the supply of trained manpower. Similarly reduction of resources may cause additional costs in the form of under used plant, which therefore inflates overhead costs; redundancy costs which take money away from services; and trained staff (eg nurses) may find that there is no job available when they have trained.

In theory these things ought to be easier to handle under the NHS reforms if purchasing authorities who are gaining money bought services from those providers who are losing and now have the surplus capacity. Experience in Birmingham and London suggests that the reverse is happening. We are now seeing services in Birmingham where the built volume standing round each bed is far greater in the areas losing capitation income thus raising their overheads and prices. This in turn leads to the gaining purchasers investing further in local services. At the time of writing the loss to providers in the South Birmingham district will cumulate to £34 million.

Fear of these costs of change has in the past produced pressure to make change very gradual. RAWP only applied to new resources. A complete change to capitation could be much more dramatic, especially if it is done quickly.

These costs of change also raise issues about stability of whatever formula is used. If the formula produces a new answer every year, even though it may be the right answer the possible benefits may be eaten up by the costs of change from year to year and result in little additional health care. These issues are rarely considered by the advocates of change but often obsess general managers and treasurers.

At the Health Service Study Group meeting in Glasgow earlier this year there seemed to be a consensus in the audience that rectifying inequalities in health must be at the core of the problem to be solved. Probably a similar consensus could be achieved around the idea that need was more important than demand. All that is left is to be sure what we mean by need and by equality of health.

There has been a long debate whether SMRs should be used as a proxy for need, or whether utilisation rates were more important, or whether we should use some relationship between the two. We are concerned with allocating money for health services because that is what Parliament has given us the money for. Many health services are directed towards treating morbidity that does not lead to death and hence is not reflected in SMRs, perhaps a strong argument for not using SMRs. On the other hand it is said that the middle classes do better out of the health service. The strongest argument for this might be that their health has improved more since the health service started than has the health of the poor. This does not mean that the health service is responsible for the gain in health. Numerous workers have shown that the poor use more health services. It may be that the health service has prevented the gap between rich and poor getting even wider, or worse still the NHS could could be responsible for the increasing gap.

The arguments for using SMRs are well rehearsed and do not need repetition here. In recent years we seem to have got stuck on the idea that the all causes under 75 SMR is a measure of preventable disease and hence might be a good proxy for need for health services. It is an attractive argument but it fails to take notice of two things. First that health authorities have to deal with many things other than preventable disease and second that the choice of age 75 is somewhat arbitrary. The graph shows how the SMR could be misused in the wrong hands. It shows SMRs calculated for different age groups in groups of districts in the West Midlands. If the SMRs calculated in this way were substituted in a resource allocation formula then the choice of age group could have a profound effect on the outcome. This is a somewhat improper analysis but it serves to give the message that there is nothing magical about the age of 75. In fact it means something different in men and women in that more men die before the age of 75 than women so the index is inherently weighted towards male events, yet it is women who consume the greater amount of NHS resources.

Figure 1 *SMRs at different ages in different districts in the West Midlands*

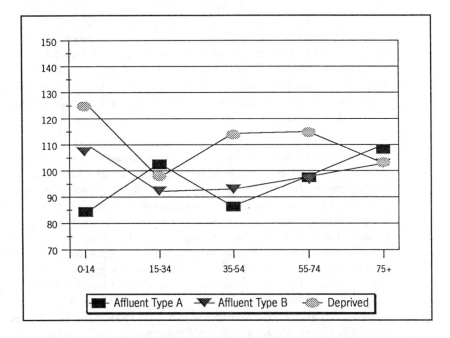

The paradoxes expand when we consider the diseases that contribute most of the deaths in the under 75 SMR. The most common preventable diseases that kill before the age of 75 are caused by smoking yet little of the resources that are spent by the NHS are dedicated to reduction of smoking. It would appear, though we do not have the data to prove it, that the use of the under 75 SMR in the allocation formula is about the same as utilising the smoking rates over the previous decade in the different populations. It might be easier to simply allocate money to health authorities in proportion to the excise tax collected on tobacco in each district.

The largest element in the allocation formula is the age weighting which is of course related to utilisation. Those who oppose the use of utilisation rates as the allocation proxy rarely seem to challenge the age weighting, though they are frequently opposed to using formulae based on the relationship between the utilisation rates and census variables.

The resource allocation business is thus full of problems but they have been made greater in the most recent reforms by the introduction of fund holding. This requires that resources be allocated equitably to populations as small as 7,000. Mortality events in populations this small occur so rarely that they cannot be used as proxies for need. One of the overriding aims of our work in Birmingham has been to find methods of studying the use and allocation of resources which would work equally well for very small populations as well as for districts within the region. Some of this work will be covered in Estelle Gilman's paper and other aspects are covered in the related poster. The only practical method that we have identified is to characterise the population in some way that refers to a larger frame of reference, like census variables. We can then aggregate the small units on this basis and explore the relationship of the aggregated groups with the usual resource allocation proxies. From there it is possible to map back down to the small units again. We have now convinced ourselves that we have a system that would work for fundholders and DHAs in an exactly parallel way. We are waiting to see if the study of Peter Smith and his colleagues at the University of York can be mapped onto this, or whether they have cracked the fundholder problem in some different way. The same principles would of course apply if DHAs or FHSAs wished to allocate resources internally to small localities, something that will be increasingly important if districts are merged into larger units. Equity will then have to be delivered by policies inside Districts.

At this conference, speakers will address some of the most difficult issues and propose their solutions and no doubt the audience will contribute as many questions as answers. In many senses there are no right answers, or none that can be irrefutably proven to be right. It has all the aspects of a truly wicked problem; it is hard to define in absolute terms and any intervention changes the problem, probably irreversibly. We have to do something and it does matter what we do. Despite some suggestions to the contrary it is obviously not a zero sum game. If it was we could allocate all the money to one health authority and be done with it. Clearly this would not produce the best health in the population. It is obvious that spending more in some areas than others is essential if we are to tackle health inequalities. But how much more, where, and how fast to change still eludes us. The new changes in the NHS mean that we will have to calculate all the numbers again. Let us hope that at the end of the conference we are better able to judge what has to go into the calculation.

Address for contact

Professor Rod K Griffiths, Director, Institute of Public & Environmental Health, Medical School, University of Birmingham, Edgbaston, Birmingham, B15 2TT.

Health Care Needs, Deprivation, and the Resource Allocation Formula

VERA CARSTAIRS, Health Service Research Networks, University of Edinburgh

This paper considers the concept of need for health care and the problems of operationalising this for the purpose of resource allocation. It reviews various measures and proxies and the case for and against incorporating social variables, including deprivation measures, into the formula. Data from the review of RAWP, and from Scotland and elsewhere, is used to illustrate the association of deprivation, and alternatives, with health (and death), and the possible implication of these findings for the formula. These analyses seek to establish an empirically-based approach to support the various elements of the formula, and specific criticisms, both theoretical and methodological, of this approach are considered.

The Resource Allocation formula (RAWP) first saw the light of day in the report of the Resource Allocation Working Party (Department of Health and Social Security, 1976). It had the aim of providing an equitable distribution of resources to health Regions according to need, and took both a theoretical and pragmatic approach (Figure 1). The first principle adopted was that the age/sex structure of a population affects need and that local populations should be weighted by national usage rates to adjust for differences between them. The second principle was that Regions will experience differential morbidity/need in addition and it was recommended that the product of the first stage should be weighted by the all-age condition-specific standard mortality ratios (SMR) for the Regions – effectively awarding a 1% increment/decrement for each unit variation in SMR over or below 100. These procedures were introduced for a number of service blocks, with a number of other factors, which need not concern us, being dealt with separately.

The SMR was adopted as a proxy for morbidity because of a number of very important qualities:

> objective; unequivocal (meaning not in doubt); reasonably accurate ('reasonably' since underlying cause is prone to some error); comprehensive; continuously available; and independent of supply.

Criticisms levied at the use of the SMR in this way however claimed that it fails to measure morbidity adequately (many important causes of morbidity do not result in death and the condition-specific SMRs omit these important needs), and fails also to encapsulate the greater health care needs of deprived populations.

5

Figure 1 *Resource Allocation 1976–77*

AIM: *equitable* distribution according to *need*

APPROACH: theoretical and pragmatic

THE FORMULA

concerned with **estimation**

1   estimate differential **relative need** based on age/sex structure and national usage rates

2   reflect differences in **morbidity** and hence relative need for health care resources:
     weight by all-ages SMR × 1 (condition-specific)

Questioning the formula:

? how good is SMR as a proxy for morbidity or need

? are there alternative measures of morbidity or need

? what should be the weighting for SMR

? should some account be taken of socio-economic factors which may influence need in addition to morbidity

? use of all-ages SMR, and condition-specific SMRs

Discussion about the formula was prompted both by the Regional Health Authorities which felt unfairly treated, and by theorists in the field of health care attracted by the challenge provoked by the formula into measurement of need (Brotherston, 1978; Forster, 1977; Palmer et al, 1979). Some Regions developed alternatives for the distribution down to Districts based on empirical analyses: North East Thames investigated hospital use by socio-economic groups (SEG), based on a census of inpatient beds, and found the ratio between SEG 1:6 remarkably constant over Districts despite differing levels of provision, and concluded that SEG would provide a good proxy for need (North East Thames Regional Health Authority, 1983); South East Thames investigated the use of ACORN groups as an alternative (South East Thames Regional Health Authority, 1985; Woods, 1982).

Small Area Modelling for Resource Allocation

The Review of RAWP (ROR) in 1985 took an essentially theoretical and empirical approach with the aims of suggesting improvements to the need measure and determining a quantitative relationship between SMR and relative need, based on evidence (Department of Health and Social Security, 1988). The model developed (Figure 2) identified the various factors influencing the use of services (Royston et al, 1992) and set out to investigate whether use of health services can inform the debate about what people need. ROR was able to take a small area approach due to the introduction of post-coding in the in-patient record system which identifies the area of residence of patients, and data were assembled for six Regions and around 3,000 wards.

Figure 2 *Factors Affecting Use of Services*

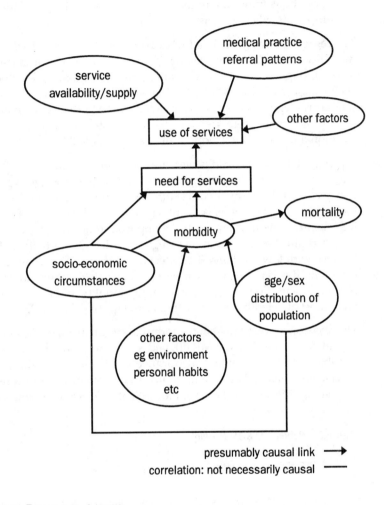

Small area modelling for health resource allocation

Source: Royston et al (1992)

Use of health services had been rejected as a valid measure of need in the original debate since at Regional and District level the use of services clearly reflects the supply available in the locality. The modelling process however advances beyond observation to estimation, and the small area approach allows the influences on bed-use to be more reliably observed, while the wider range found in all the measures provides a sounder statistical basis for the modelling procedures. The approach also disposes of much of the criticism of the identification of hospital use as a need measure (Morgan et al, 1987) since within an area populations compete for the same supply of beds so that the influence of other factors (including socio-economic) can be more reliably observed (variation in supply between areas still needs to be taken into account). Some critics have claimed that deprived populations exhibit greater use of hospital services because they are located in inner cities close to the hospital (Morgan et al, 1987). While this may be true in a few locations it is manifestly not observed in many cities where large hospitals serve populations which are geographically widespread and socially diverse and where wide variations in use are found for sub-groups of the population for which the supply of beds is effectively constant.

The regression analysis aimed to explain variation in discharges in terms of mortality and social factors, taking the availability of and distance to beds into account (Figure 3). The key results from the model were the estimated coefficients of 0.44 for SMR0–74 (all causes) and of 0.0026 for the Jarman UPA8 (underprivileged area) score, over and above SMR (bed availability taken into account); ie there were residual discharge ratios explained by deprivation additional to mortality (Coopers and Lybrand, 1988).

As you will know the results were imported into the formula with a reduced weighting for SMR (in fact √SMR0–74), and with any weighting for deprivation excluded (Department of Health, 1989), presumably on the grounds that the basis for analysis was insufficiently comprehensive. The results for Regions are shown in Figure 4: the application of the reduced weighting of course diminishes the allocation to regions with high mortality and increases it to those with low mortality. The effect of the deprivation factor although less pronounced was nevertheless important; in particular it would have provided some compensation to regions with high mortality and high deprivation that were most affected by the reduction in the gearing for SMR.

The decision to use SMR74 in the formula was made on the basis of its greater explanatory power (than SMRall), and also on account of its greater inherent variability. The report of ROR also argued that in the elderly there may exist an inverse relationship between mortality and health problems (as recognised in the use of SMR0-64 in the formula for Scotland (Scottish Home and Health

Figure 3   *Review of RAWP 1986*

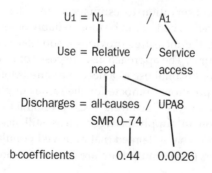

APPROACH: theoretical and empirical

AIM: provide empirical evidence, improve measure of need

METHODS: small area analysis based on 6 Regions with c. 3000 wards

FORMULA: regression model: (simplified)

$$U_1 = N_1 \qquad / \quad A_1$$

Use = Relative   / Service
     need   access

Discharges = all-causes / UPA8
          SMR 0–74

b-coefficients   0.44   0.0026

Figure 4 *Effect of formula variants on regional target funding**

Region	% change using weighted SMR75	% change using weighted SMR75 and social deprivation
Northern	−1.3	−0.3
Yorkshire	−0.6	0.7
Trent	−0.8	−1.6
E Anglia	−0.1	−1.0
NW Thames	1.9	1.7
NE Thames	0.8	1.9
SE Thames	1.1	1.7
SW Thames	1.6	−0.2
Wessex	2.8	1.4
Oxford	0.1	−1.5
S Western	1.9	0.5
W Midlands	−1.7	−1.7
Mersey	−1.1	−0.5
N Western	−2.6	−0.9

*1988–89 figures.

Source: Royston et al (1992)

Department, 1977) but – since the SMR74 is applied to the total age/sex weighted estimates produced at the first stage of the process – this proposition was not carried to its logical conclusion.

Further analysis of the same data set at District level by Jarman et al (unpublished) and by Hancock et al (1991) using data for the three Regions with the most reliable data confirmed a coefficient for SMR considerably below unity.

A similar analysis in Scotland examined data for virtually all postcode sectors (n = 898), with a very few exclusions due to very small populations and sectors with a large institutional component (Carstairs and Morris, 1989). The major difference to the English data set was the use of bed-days rather than discharges as a measure of utilisation; also the comprehensive nature of the data-set provided information on all cross-border flows so that a catchment-based bed supply measure could be reliably calculated for both large and small areas. Distances to services (DIS) and bed supply (SUP) were calculated as two separate measures, a desirable feature since the correlation with distance is negative while that with supply is positive. The correlation was stronger with supply for bed-days and for distance with discharges but as in the English analysis these measures proved fairly insignificant in explaining variability.

Figure 5 shows that although distance and supply have some influence on the R^2 they have little impact on the b-coefficient for SMR, but that this is radically affected by the introduction of the deprivation variable DEP, into the regression, since DEP and SMR are highly correlated. The explanatory power of these four variables is weak for all beds but moderately strong for the age-group 0–64.

The results for Scotland using SMR74 may also be compared with those emerging from ROR (Figure 6) and show that the coefficients from these two very different data sets are very similar (Carstairs and Morris, 1989).

Figure 5 *Regression of bed-days on SMR, DIS, SUP and DEP (Scotland)*

All beds, SMR all

Var	Simple r	R²	R² % change	b– [a] coeff. SMR
SMR	0.257	0.066	6.6	0.62
DIS	0.061	0.075	0.9	0.65
SUP	0.121	0.099	2.4	0.70
DEP	0.252	0.108	0.9	0.46

Acute beds 0–64, SMR64

Var	Simple r	R²	R² % change	b– [a] coeff. SMR
SMR	0.563	0.317	31.7	0.54
DIS	−0.063	0.317	0.0	0.54
SUP	0.226	0.409	9.2	0.57
DEP	0.604	0.475	6.6	0.29

[a] shows change in SMR coefficient with progressive addition of other variables

r = linear correlation coefficient

Source: Carstairs and Morris (1989)

Figure 6 *Predicting Discharges and Bed-Days*
Comparison of English (ROR) and Scottish Regression Models

	England		Scotland	
	R	b	R	b
SMR74	0.36	0.44	0.096	0.52
DEP/DOE	0.03	0.0058	0.003	0.0052
UPA 7/8	0.05	0.0026	0.009	0.0025
	(2-stage model)		(scales differ)	

Source: Carstairs and Morris (1989)
See source for definition of variable terms

The English analysis reported little association between length of stay and either SMR or UPA8 (underprivileged area) and hence the decision to focus on discharges. This result runs counter to expectation that one of the effects of poorer social circumstances would be to prolong stay in hospital, and the Scottish data certainly produced a positive association (Carstairs and Morris, 1991). Bed-days would appear to be an inherently more precise measure of resource use and requirement than discharges, less susceptible perhaps to vagaries in practice.

Measuring Health Care Needs

In the context of measuring need a number of criticisms of these analyses may be considered (Carr-Hill, 1989; Mays, 1987 and 1989; Morgan et al, 1987). Perhaps the key consideration which has attracted most comment is the question:

• can hospital use provide a good proxy for morbidity and need?

The main problem in this area is the interdependence of supply and use, a consideration which led the original working party to reject bed-use as a valid and reliable measure. At Regional level of course the picture is confounded but the small-area analysis overcomes much of the problem since a constant level of bed supply is available to populations which differ widely in their social circumstances, and compete for these beds. The use of a bed availability term in the regression models (to take account of variation in supply between regions) has also dealt with this problem. Critics who argue that the logical conclusion of this approach would be that the amount of resources required would be the amount consumed overlook the fact that the pooling of the data and the statistical modelling ensures that what emerges is estimation and not replication.

I would like to deal together with the other three common criticisms of use as a measure of need:
- factors other than need affect demand and use
- current use provides no indication of appropriate use
- measurement of the distribution of morbidity should be addressed directly rather than relying on ever more indirect proxies for health resource need

Of course demand for hospital (inpatient) care is mediated by many influences other than morbidity – patient behaviour, GP and consultant practice, fashions in care, the availability of effective treatment, alternative services etc (see Figure 2). We should consider that variations in demand due to patient behaviour and doctor practice are part of the realities of the situation and that actual rather than theoretical demands are what the service has to meet. These may change with greater understanding but in the meantime these factors constitute part of the demand process; it seems unlikely these variations will be distributed between regions other than at random.

The influence on demand of alternative forms of care is another matter; regions with a small part of demand met by private care are likely to be losers in any formula which is based on national rates of utilisation, while those which are high users will receive a bonus.

In relation to appropriate use there are obvious conditions involving the use of sophisticated techniques and equipment, specialised facilities and environments where the need for inpatient care is beyond doubt, but there are equally many other conditions for which considerable elasticity exists and alternative forms of care may be used. While morbidity remains the same resource need may also vary as developments in medical technology and expertise bring conditions within the realm of effective care and possibilities of treatment expand: we may think of coronary by-pass surgery, joint replacement, renal dialysis. For others the mode (and perhaps resource cost) is reduced; eg tuberculosis is treated by medication and not long bed rest; gastric ulcers by medication and not surgery; keyhole surgery results in a shorter stay in hospital; many more conditions are treated on a day-care basis. From this brief list it is clear that the equation between morbidity and resource need is a shifting scene. Moreover since – 'For more than 80% of medical conditions and large numbers of surgical conditions the need for hospital care is not clearly defined and there is little consensus as to the appropriate form of management' (Wennberg, 1986) the identification of appropriate care also presents a considerable challenge. The measurement of appropriate need is unlikely to be attained in the short term although met demand and appropriate care will surely come closer together in the future assisted by growing understanding of the effectiveness of treatment, by purchaser requirements and by the development of profiles of care.

No one could disagree that we should pursue the measurement of morbidity directly or argue that a valid, reliable and comprehensive measure of morbidity presents an alluring prospect, but at present a large gap exists between this prospect and the capabilities for measurement. The question on limiting long-term illness and handicap was included in the 1991 Census with the intention that it might fill this gap. As most people will know by now the levels reported are lower than on the General Household Survey (GHS) giving rise to much speculation about the reasons for this and whether it can be attributed to a variation in the wording used. Figure 7 shows the levels reported in regions from the Census question (OPCS, 1993a) compared with data from the GHS (OPCS, 1993b). Of course results from the latter are subject to sampling error, and the distribution varies from year to year; lower levels of reporting in the Census and lack of agreement between the two measures nevertheless raise some doubts about the reliability of the census measure, based as it is on subjective opinion about health state. In the meantime perhaps we should regard with more doubt the much-stated proposition and widely-held belief that morbidity is a good indicator of need.

Figure 7 *Measuring Need*
Long-standing limiting illness/disability/chronic illness
by Region: percent of population all ages, both sexes

Region	Census 1991*	General Household Survey 1991
Wales	16.4	22
North	15.0	22
North West	14.1	18
Yorkshire	13.5	18
Scotland	12.9	17
West Midlands	12.4	17
East Midlands	11.9	19
South West	11.6	16
East Anglia	11.0	19
South East	10.5	16

*in private households

Source: OPCS 1993a and OPCS 1993b

Perhaps the Health Survey for England (Department of Health, 1993) which incorporates objective physiological measures and blood analyses among its variables will begin to provide information which we can confidently believe reflects genuine morbidity differences; enhanced sample sizes in 1993 and 1994 will provide data at regional level but interpreting these will still present problems due to sampling error.

But even when we finally arrive at a suitable measure of morbidity are we then in a position to say unequivocally what this means in terms of need for health care? 'Funding formulae require relative need for services to be expressed in resource terms. Mortality and morbidity are clearly relevant to assessing need but they do not in themselves provide a translation into the language of resources' (Royston et al, 1992). Argument about the appropriate gearing for SMR exemplifies this problem; no measure of morbidity will automatically overcome this problem, and the element of use of services must surely remain an essential ingredient of any equation.

The Relationship Between Deprivation and Health Care Needs

This brings us to the final element in measuring need that I wish to consider:

- the issue of whether to take into account the socio-economic circumstances of populations; ie a component for deprivation

The influence of deprivation is generally considered relevant since deprived populations may exhibit:

- excess morbidity not reflected in mortality
- a lower threshold for admission to hospital
- longer stays in hospital
- greater resource costs to provide equivalent programmes of care; eg more cost to get deprived populations to engage in preventive care

The stance originally taken by the Department of Health was that tackling deprivation was not the business of the health services. The counter-argument is that surely the health service should concern itself with the effects on health of deprivation, especially as there appears to be ample evidence of that relationship! Although ROR identified deprivation (in the form of the under-privileged area (UPA) score) as an added influence on the demand for hospital care (Coopers and Lybrand, 1988) there was no element for deprivation included in the revised formula. One factor may have been the lack of any consensus between proponents on the constituents of an index (Figure 8), and another the view taken that because all deprivation measures are on an artificial scale it was not possible to describe the relationship between deprivation and use of health services with the same confidence as was possible for mortality (Department of Health and Social Security, 1988).

A number of deprivation measures were in fact tested in ROR other than the Jarman UPA score, with the Townsend, Department of the Environment and Jarman scores performing equally well but with the results suggesting that different measures might be more appropriate within Regions (Coopers and Lybrand, 1988). The Townsend index was considered not to include among its variables many of the social circumstances likely to affect decisions on patterns of treatment. The Jarman score was preferred to DoE on the basis that it was drawn up in the context of need for health care, and not of urban policy – and had slightly greater explanatory power (Department of Health and Social Security, 1988). In the event a component for deprivation was not included in the revised formula (Department of Health, 1989).

Figure 8 *Range of Variables in Selected Deprivation Measures*

	DEP	JAR	TOWN	DOE	SDD
Unemployment	×	×	×	×	×
youth unemployment					×
No car	×		×		
Low social class	×				
unskilled		×			×
Overcrowding	×	×	×	×	
below occupancy norm					×
Not owner-occupied			×		
Lacking amenities				×	×
Single parent		×		×	×
Under age 5		×			
Elderly households					×
Lone pensioners		×		×	
1-year immigrants		×			
Ethnic minorities		×		×	
Vacant dwellings				×	
Level and access (old)				×	
Level and access (< 5)				×	
Pemanent sickness				×	
Large households				×	

Source: Morris and Carstairs (1991)

Figure 9 *Association of morbidity measures with DEP and SMR: Scotland*

	DEP	SMR			
		All	0–64	0–74	65+
SMR all	0.75		0.81	0.88	0.90
0–64	0.76			0.90	0.48
0–74	0.78				0.67
65+	0.53				
Permsick	0.84	0.70	0.74		
Tempsick	0.75	0.61	0.62		
Low B'weight	0.59	0.45	0.45		
Perinatal Deaths	0.36				
Cancer Regs.	0.38	0.34	0.32		
—lung	0.74				
MI admissions	0.42	0.40	0.43		
—first	0.49				
—0–64	0.54	0.43	0.47		

Since that time there has been a fair amount of activity within Regions concerned with methods of distribution within their areas – and we can look forward to hearing details from some of these later in the conference.

Data for Scotland show very clearly the strong association of the Scottish DEP score with mortality, with DEP exhibiting slightly stronger association with morbidity measures than SMR (Figure 9). The association of individual census variables (Figure 10, Scottish data) indicates the very weak association of many of the variables included inthe Jarman score with a range of sickness measures (Morris and Carstairs, 1991). We can see in the next table (Figure 11) that the Jarman score itself also exhibits much weaker correlation with these sickness measures than either the Scottish deprivation measure (DEP) or the Townsend score (TOWN), but that Jarman (JAR) has greater explanatory power in respect of discharges and acute bed-days used by those aged 65 and over. Part of this greater explanation is likely to lie in the inclusion in the Jarman UPA score of a variable for the elderly living alone, with the strongest weighting of any of the eight variables which make up the index (Jarman, 1983).

As with morbidity, definition and measurement of deprivation presents problems – and as with morbidity the concept and measurement of deprivation has provided an arena for much debate, discussion and adverse comment (Carr-Hill, 1988): the selection of variables from the census is arbitrary and the statistical treatment not consistent; selection is constrained by variables available from the census, with this source becoming available only at 10-yearly intervals. Nevertheless the overwhelming evidence of greater need in deprived populations (which I have had time only to touch upon today) will surely provide the spur to further examination of these relationships and the search for more timely indicators.

Perhaps one final word: Resource-Allocation is focussed on meeting needs for care; I would like to leave you with the thought that health care policy should

Figure 10 *Correlation of census variables*
with health measures

Deprivation Index*	Census Variable	SMR 0–64	SMR 65+	Perm Sick	Temp Sick	Scot DEP
ST	No car	0.739	0.492	0.800	0.684	0.916
ST	Unemployment	0.734	0.519	0.804	0.738	0.932
STJ	Overcrowded	0.651	0.515	0.729	0.730	0.916
SJ	Social Class IV/V	0.616	0.414	0.699	0.584	0.861
J	One-parent	0.477	0.349	0.492	0.429	0.713
T	Not owner occupied	0.545	0.412	0.644	0.564	0.777
J	Lone pensioner	0.104	0.038	0.134	−0.049	−0.025
J	Age < 5	0.019	0.110	−0.117	0.065	0.070
J	Change/address	−0.161	−0.100	−0.348	−0.301	−0.285
J	Ethnic origin	−0.050	−0.024	−0.160	−0.112	−0.116

* S – Scotland (Carstairs)
  T – Townsend
  J – Jarman

Source: Morris and Carstairs (1991)

Figure 11 *Correlation of Three Deprivation Measures with Mortality, Sickness and Hospital Use Variables*

		DEP	JAR	TOWN
SMR				
	0–64	0.75	0.68	0.73
	0–74	0.78	0.71	0.77
	65+	0.53	0.49	0.53
Permanently sick		0.83	0.67	0.80
Temporarily sick		0.75	0.60	0.73
Bed-days				
Acute				
	0–64	0.60	0.63	0.56
	65+	0.10	0.18	0.07
Discharges				
Acute				
	0–64	0.49	0.53	0.45
	65+	0.16	0.20	0.13

Source: Morris and Carstairs (1991)

be concerned with changing needs as much as with meeting needs, a focus which might merit even more positive discrimination in funding towards deprived populations in order to reduce inequalities in health rather than merely providing for needs to be met.

References

Brotherston Sir John (ed.) (1978). Morbidity and its relationship to Resource Allocation, London, HMSO.

Carr-Hill R A (1988). Revising the RAWP formula: indexing deprivation and modelling demand, York University Centre for Health Economics, Discussion Paper 41.

Carr-Hill R A (1989). Allocating resources to health care; RAWP is dead – long live RAWP, Hlth Policy: 135–44.

Carstairs V and Morris R (1989). Deprivation, mortality and resource allocation, Community Medicine, 11,4: 364–72.

Carstairs V and Morris R (1991). Deprivation and health in Scotland, Aberdeen University Press.

Coopers and Lybrand (1988). Integrated analysis for the review of RAWP, London, Coopers and Lybrand.

Department of Health (1989). Working for patients; funding and contracts for hospital services, Working paper No 2, London, HMSO.

Department of Health (1993). Health Survey for England 1991, London, HMSO.

Department of Health and Social Security (1976). Sharing Resources for Health in England; Report of the Resource Allocation Working Party, London, HMSO.

Department of Health and Social Security (1988). Review of the Resource Allocation Working Party; Final Report by the NHS Management Board, London, DHSS.

Forster D P (1977). Mortality, morbidity and resource allocation, Lancet, 1: 997–8.

Hancock K E, Holden D R, Swales J R (1991). Consistency of the spatial allocation of NHS hospital resources: econometric analysis, Applied Economics, (23): 1623–36.

Jarman B (1983). Identification of underprivileged areas, Br Med J, 286: 1705–8.

Jarman B, Rice P and White P. Integrated analysis for the review of RAWP; District Health Authority Data for England (unpublished).

Mays N B. (1987). Reviewing RAWP; measuring morbidity for resource allocation, Br Med J, 295: 703–6.

Mays N (1989). NHS resource allocation after the 1989 White Paper; a critique of research for the RAWP review, Community Medicine, 11, 3: 173–86.

Morgan M, Mays N and Holland W (1987). Can hospital use be a measure of need for hospital care? J Epidemiol Commun Hlth 41: 269–74.

Morris R and Carstairs V (1991). Which deprivation? – a comparison of selected deprivation indexes, J Pub Hlth Med: 13, 4: 318–26.

Office of Population Censuses and Surveys and General Register Office (Scotland) (1993a). 1991 Census, Limiting Long-term Illness, Great Britain, Topic Monitor, London, OPCS.

Office of Population Censuses and Surveys. (1993b) General Household Survey.

North East Thames Regional Health Authority (1983). Patient census study – social factor analysis, London, NETRHA.

Palmer S, West P, Patrick D and Glynn M (1979). Mortality indices in resource allocation, Community Medicine, 1: 275–81.

Royston G D H, Hurst J W, Lister E G and Stewart P A (1992). Modelling the use of health services by populations of small areas to inform the allocation of central resources to larger regions, Socio-Econ. Planning Sci. 26, 3: 169–80.

Scottish Home and Health Department (1977). Scottish Health Authorities Revenue Equalisation (SHARE); Report of the Working Party on Revenue Resource Allocation, Edinburgh, HMSO.

South East Thames Regional Health Authority (1985). ACORN and RAWP; an allowance for social deprivation, Bexhill-on-Sea, Statistics and Operational Research Department, SETRHA.

Wennberg J, (1986). What rate is right? New Eng J Med, 314: 310–11.

Woods K J (1982). Social deprivation and resource allocation in the Thames Regional Health Authorities, in Health Research Group, Contemporary perspectives on health and health care. Occasional Paper No 20. London: Department of Geography and Earth Science, Queen Mary College, University of London, 71–85.

Address for contact

Dr Vera Carstairs, National Co-ordinator of Health Services Research Networks, University of Edinburgh, 12 Buccleuch Place, Edinburgh, EH8 9LW.

Deprivation and Resource Allocation in the West Midlands Regional Health Authority

ESTELLE GILMAN, LILLIAN SOMERVAILLE and ROD GRIFFITHS,
Institute of Public and Environmental Health, University of Birmingham

SUMMARY

Currently, the Department of Health allocates resources for Hospital and Community Health Services (HCHS) to individual Regional Health Authorities (RHAs) using a formula which does not include a weighting for social deprivation. The principle guiding the process of resource allocation to RHAs is that there should be equal access (or at least equal provision) of health care for equal need. This principle should also underlie the way in which a RHA distributes resources for HCHS of its constituent District Health Authorities (DHAs), and this paper outlines one approach to this problem in the West Midlands.

Taking hospital utilisation as a proxy for need for health care, the relationship between utilisation and factors known to be related to morbidity, ie socio-economic deprivation and mortality, has been examined. Data on hospital episodes, deaths, populations and Townsend scores have been assembled for each of the 826 electoral wards in the West Midlands RHA, and have been used in a regression analysis. Wards with similar Townsend scores were combined into 14 population groups and this aggregated data used in a further regression analysis. It was found that Townsend score is at least as good an explanatory variable as SMR, and that hospital utilisation significantly increases with increasing Townsend score. The same relationship between utilisation and Townsend score was also found for individual wards within each DHA. Further work has shown that this relationship is also found at the smaller area level of the enumeration district, and it is proposed that this methodology would lend itself to the problem of equitable allocation of resources to GP Fundholders for the purchase of secondary care.

19

Introduction

The methods by which the Department of Health has allocated resources for Hospital and Community Health Services (HCHS) to individual Regional Health Authorities (RHAs) have been subject to much change and review. In 1976 there was the report of the Resource Allocation Working Party (RAWP) (DHSS, 1976) and more recently a review of RAWP was carried out (DHSS, 1986). The last report of this review recommended that allocations should be based on a combination of factors, including the region's all causes SMR (ages 0–75 years), and socio-economic status (as measured by the Jarman score) (DHSS, 1988). However, the version of the formula currently used by the Department of Health for calculating regional allocations does not include any weighting for social deprivation. A further re-examination of the formula has just been completed for the Department of Health, and is the subject of a later paper in this volume (Carr-Hill et al).

Objectives and Approach

Most of the recent debate has concerned the issue of allocating resources to RHAs. The methods by which the individual RHAs then distribute those resources among their constituent District Health Authorities (DHAs) vary. Some simply apply the national formula, while others have devised their own processes. What will be reported here is one approach which has been investigated in the West Midlands.

First one must define the underlying problem. What is it that all these allocation processes are trying to achieve? Basically, the aim is to distribute resources for health services according to the need for those health services, ie to ensure equal access (or equal provision) of health care for equal need.

Putting this into the context of an RHA trying to allocate resources fairly to its constituent DHAs, the RHA must know each DHA's need for health care. One indicator of the need for health care, but not a perfect one, is the utilisation of hospital services. But it would not be appropriate to use current utilisation as a direct measure of need for health services, because the utilisation of an individual district may not necessarily be what it should be. One must instead examine the overall relationship, across the whole region, between utilisation and factors such as mortality and socio-economic status, which are known to be associated with morbidity and the need for health care. If this is done by regression analysis, the resulting equation can be used to calculate the predicted utilisation of an area, for its given age, sex, mortality and socio-economic profile. This predicted utilisation can then be used in the calculation of weighted populations for the purposes of resource allocation on a capitation basis.

Materials and Methods

The following information was assembled for the 826 local authority wards in the West Midlands RHA:

- all causes hospital in-patient episodes (1989/90) (all finished consultant episodes, excluding episodes for normal maternity, mental illness and mental handicap)
- all causes standardised mortality ratios (1986–90)
- Townsend scores (1981 census).

Standardised in-patient episode ratios (SERs) were calculated by indirect standardisation, using the regional episode rate as the standard. Standardised mortality ratios were calculated by indirect standardisation using national mortality rates. The socio-economic status, or deprivation, of each ward was indicated by its Townsend score, which was calculated by standardising and normalising using the regional means and standard deviations for each of its component variables, ie
  % of private households with no car;
  % of private households which are not owner-occupied;
  % of private households with more than one person per room;
  % of economically active residents who are unemployed.

Townsend score was chosen because it is an established and recognised indicator of material deprivation, and it was not our intention to enter the potential minefield of constructing a new indicator (which would then only be of direct relevance to the West Midlands population). The Townsend score is also to be preferred as it does not include demographic factors, such as proportion of single parent familes, or lone pensioners, which simply indicate those *at risk* of deprivation but not necessarily those who are actually deprived (Townsend et al, 1988; Carstairs and Morris, 1991). Our preliminary analyses had also shown that it performed as well as, if not better than other indices eg Department of the Environment Z-scores (Department of the Environment, 1983), and the Jarman score, which was not designed as a measure of deprivation, but as an indicator of GP workload (Jarman, 1983; Jarman, 1984).

Linear regression analysis was used to model the relationship between standardised hospital episode ratio (SER) as the dependent variable, and SMR and Townsend score as the independent variables. Analyses were carried out at the individual ward level, and also using a set of 14 groups produced by combining data from wards with the same unit level of Townsend score. This aggregation produced groups homogeneous for social variables, which contained geographically non-contiguous wards distributed across the West Midlands RHA. This not only ensured larger sample sizes for analysis, but also should serve to reduce the effects on hospital in-patient activity of factors such as variations between DHAs in the level of supply of hospital services and in local referral and treatment practices.

Results

The results of the analyses, both at individual and at aggregated ward level, are shown in Table 1. The goodness of fit of each model is indicated by the value of R^2, the proportion of variation in the data that is explained by the model. The Townsend score is at least as good an explanatory variable as SMR. However, when both Townsend and SMR were included in the model, there

Table 1 *Results of regression analysis of SER(1989/90) on Townsend score and SMR(1986–90). West Midlands RHA. People, all ages.*

	Individual wards			Aggregated wards	
Variable	Coefficient	P		Coefficient	P
MODEL 1	**SER=a+b(TOW)**				
Intercept	91.65	0.0001		94.97	0.0001
Townsend	3.37	0.0001		3.18	0.0001
Adjusted R²	0.24			Adjusted R²	0.98
MODEL 2	**SER=a+c(SMR)**				
Intercept	58.85	0.0001		−126.70	0.0002
SMR	0.32	0.0001		2.15	0.0001
Adjusted R²	0.12			Adjusted R²	0.87
MODEL 3	**SER=a+b(TOW)+c(SMR)**				
Intercept	65.15	0.0001		65.25	0.0184
Townsend	3.08	0.0001		2.81	0.0001
SMR	0.25	0.0001		0.29	0.2337
Adjusted R²	0.31			Adjusted R²	0.98

was little improvement in goodness of fit. The significant relationship between increase in hospital utilisation and increase in Townsend score is shown in Figure 1 for individual wards, and in Figure 2 for aggregated wards. The relationship is very tight indeed for aggregated data, demonstrating how much the ward grouping technique has acted to reduce the variance or 'noise' in the data.

Figure 1 *Regression of SERs of all causes hospital in-patient episodes on Townsend score. Individual wards, West Midlands RHA, people all ages. Model: SER=91.65+3.37 (TOW)*

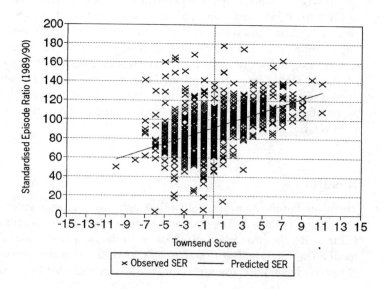

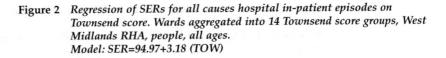

Figure 2 *Regression of SERs for all causes hospital in-patient episodes on Townsend score. Wards aggregated into 14 Townsend score groups, West Midlands RHA, people, all ages.*
Model: SER=94.97+3.18 (TOW)

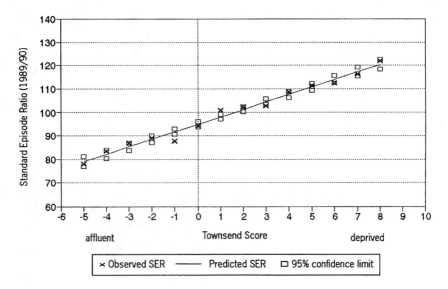

Discussion

The use of census data is often criticised because it is updated only every 10 years. The work reported here used data from the 1981 Census and 1989/90 hospital in-patient episodes because these were the latest available at the time. Since then, 1991 Census data and 1991/92 hospital data have become available. Initial re-working of the analyses presented here are showing the same kinds of relationships and levels of statistical significance as seen in the earlier data. A crude comparison of wards and their scores (after adjustments to cope with some of the major ward boundary changes) showed that the distribution of Townsend scores across the wards within the West Midlands RHA did not change substantially between the two censuses, 83% of wards (and 88% of people) changed Townsend score by 1 unit or less (Figure 3).

The aggregation of wards from different DHAs was expected to reduce the possible confounding effects of different supply levels and local referral practices. However, no attempt was made to explicitly model these effects. Instead, the regression analyses were repeated separately for wards within individual DHAs. It was assumed that wards belonging to a particular DHA were subject to similar supply constraints and referral practices. A statistical comparison of the models obtained revealed that the same regional slope could be fitted to wards within each DHA, ie the relationship between Townsend score and hospital utilisation within each DHA was not significantly different to that shown by the region as a whole.

The problem of ecological fallacy, where results from analyses at the population level are used to infer that the same relationships exist for the individ-

Figure 3 *Change in Townsend score between 1981 and 1991 censuses for wards in the West Midlands RHA.*
Values shown are differences in unit level of score ie (1991 score – 1981 score).

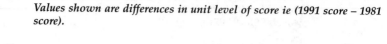

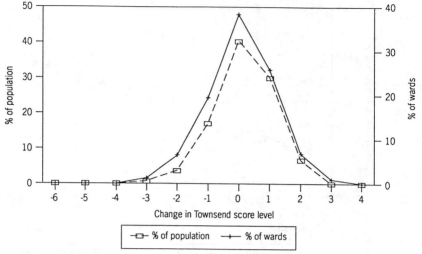

uals who make up that population, still remains. However, further work which is described later in this volume (Billingham et al) has confirmed that the relationship between SER and Townsend score (using the 1991 census) is also found at the smaller area level of the enumeration district (ED).

Finally, the confirmation of this same relationship at the ED level, where EDs were aggregated on the basis of Townsend score, means that in principle this methodology could be applied to the problem of determining the equitable allocation of resources to GP Fundholders for the purchase of secondary care. The Townsend scores calculated at the ED level should be more robust than SMRs because they will be based on larger numbers of events. EDs belonging to a particular practice could be assembled and weighted populations produced for them in a fashion exactly analogous with the calculation of weighted populations for DHAs.

References

Carstairs, V and Morris, R (1991). Deprivation and health in Scotland. Aberdeen University Press.

Department of the Environment (1983). Urban deprivation. Information Note No. 2. HMSO, London.

Department of Health and Social Security (1976). Sharing resources for health in England. Report of the Resource Allocation Working Party. HMSO, London.

Department of Health and Social Security (1986). Review of the Resource Allocation Working Party Formula: interim report by the NHS Management Board. HMSO, London.

Department of Health and Social Security (1988). Final report by the NHS Management Board of the review of the resource allocation formula. HMSO, London.

Jarman, B (1983). Identification of underprivileged areas. British Medical Journal, 286, 1705-1709.

Jarman, B (1984). Underprivileged areas: validation and distribution of scores. British Medical Journal, 289, 1587–1592.

Townsend, P, Phillimore, P and Beattie, A (1988). Health and deprivation: Inequality and the North. Routledge, London.

Address for contact

Dr Estelle Gilman, Institute of Public & Environmental Health, Medical School, The University of Birmingham, Edgbaston, Birmingham, B15 2TT.

Small Area Utilization and Resource Allocation

ROY CARR-HILL, GEOFF HARDMAN, STEPHEN MARTIN, STUART
PEACOCK, TREVOR A SHELDON and PETER SMITH, University of
York

SUMMARY

A team at the University of York has been undertaking an analysis of
small area utilization of inpatient hospital services. The work has been
commissioned by the Department of Health as part of its review of
weighted capitation formulae. The study has sought to identify the
important determinants of utilization, and has examined the importance
of socio-economic conditions, health status and supply considerations
in forming demand for health care. The paper presents some of the
results from the study, and assesses their relevance to resource allocation at national and local level.

Introduction

This paper describes a study undertaken at the University of York which
sought to identify the principal determinants of hospital inpatient utilization
in England. The study formed part of the Department of Health's review of the
weighted capitation formula used to distribute Hospital and Community
Health Service (HCHS) funds to Regional Health Authorities. The paper
contains only the briefest outline of the study. After a discussion of the
theoretical framework of the study the methods are described. Results are then
discussed, and the paper ends with a description of how they could be used to
develop a formula for distributing Hospital and Community Health Service
funds to health authorities. At the time of writing (October 1993), the study
had not been completed, so the results presented here are provisional. Full
details are given in the study report (Carr-Hill et al, 1993).

Theoretical Framework

The purpose of the study was to develop an empirically based model of
demand for health care. Two types of determinant of demand were considered
to be important: the health care needs of the population, and the supply of
health care facilities. Needs were broadly interpreted, to include indirect social

26

determinants of demand for health care as well as direct measures of health status. The inclusion of supply considerations reflected the widely held belief that the availability of health care services might affect demand for those services in two ways: first, supplier-induced demand might stimulate utilization, and second, limitations of supply might constrain utilization.

Figure 1 *The simplified model of demand for health care*

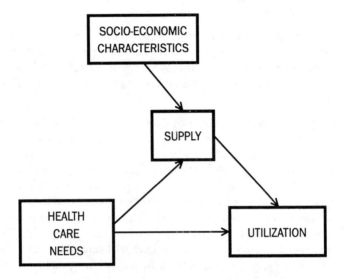

The requirement was to build a statistical model relating utilization to indicators of needs and supply. However, central to the study was the insight that – as well as influencing utilization – supply may itself also have been influenced by utilization and needs in the past. That is, although it is possible to say that utilization U_i in area i is a function of needs N_i and supply S_i in area i:

$$U_i = f(N_i, S_i) \quad \textbf{1}$$

it is also plausible to suggest that supply might in turn be influenced by utilization, needs and possibly other determinants, labelled X_i, as follows:

$$S_i = g(U_i, N_i, X_i) \quad \textbf{2}$$

If this situation obtains, it is inappropriate to employ conventional ordinary least squares regression methods to estimate (1). Instead, it is necessary to use methods such as two stage least squares to take account of the simultaneous determination of U and S.

Methods

The units of analysis used in the study were 4,985 'synthetic wards', small areas with average populations of about 10,000 covering the whole of England. These small areas were electoral wards, aggregated where necessary so that none had a population of less than 5,000. For each synthetic ward, data were assembled relating to the need for health care, the supply of health services, and the utilization made of inpatient services (including day cases).

The needs variables comprised detailed demographic data prepared by the OPCS, health status variables, and broader social and economic variables derived from the 1991 Census of Population. The health status variables included standardized mortality ratios (SMRs), standardized illness ratios derived from the Census, and low birth weight data. A total of 37 socio-economic variables thought to be possible influences on demand for health care were abstracted from the Census.

Four supply variables were created, reflecting the availability of health services to the ward's population. They sought to measure the accessibility of NHS inpatient facilities, the accessibility of GP services, the provision of residential and nursing homes, and the accessibility of private inpatient facilities.

Utilization rates, standardized for age and sex, were calculated from the 1990/91 Hospital Episode Statistics (HES), a database of all hospital inpatient episodes (including day cases). The study team had available estimates of fixed and daily episode costs for 12 specialty groups prepared by East Cheshire Statistical Analysis Consultancy. These were used to attach a cost to each episode, and thereby measure a ward's utilization in terms of costs. Two types of cost were calculated for each episode: the *standard cost* is the national average cost for a particular age, sex and specialty group; the *estimated cost* is the specialty-specific cost for the length of stay of the episode. Standard costs seek to remove local variations in policy and practice from the utilization measure, but do not capture variations in lengths of stay brought about by variations in needs. For this reason, the study team's advisers recommended the use of estimated costs as the basis for most of the analysis.

A ward's utilization was modelled as a function of supply and needs, using two stage least squares regression methods. Three separate models were estimated, for acute, long stay and maternity specialty groups. The long stay specialty group comprised geriatric medicine, psychiatry and mental handi-cap specialties. Throughout the models were found to perform better when natural logarithms were taken of all variables.

In the first instance, in addition to the supply variables, a large number of potential determinants of health care needs were included in the model. The initial selection of needs variables was made by successively adding needs variables on the basis of maximum correlation with the residuals from the existing model. In this way an attempt was made to minimize the problem of multicollinearity. When none of the remaining needs variables showed statistically significant correlation with the residuals, a small number of additional variables that had not been included, but which were thought *a priori* to be related to health care needs were added to the set of needs variables. The model was then progressively restricted by omitting needs variables on the basis of lack of statistical significance. This process was continued until deletion of another variable would have altered the model significantly in a statistical sense. Tests were made to ensure that the model was statistically well specified, and that the two stage least squares method was justified in preference to ordinary least squares.

Results

As noted above, all results are provisional at the time of writing. The purpose of this section is therefore to give an indication of the sorts of models that are emerging from the analysis. A parsimonious model for acute specialties has been identified which includes the following variables:

ACCNHS	Access to NHS acute beds
ACCGPS	Access to general practitioners
HOMES*	Proportion of population aged 75+ not in nursing or residential homes
ACCPRI	Access to private hospital beds
DENSITY	Persons divided by hectares
MANUAL	Proportion in manual social classes
OLDALONE	Proportion of pensionable age living alone
S_CARER	Proportion of dependants in single carer households
UNEMP	Proportion of economically active unemployed
SMR074	Standardized mortality ratio (SMR) for ages 0–74

It should be noted that many of the needs variables are highly colinear. As a result, the precise choice of needs variables is somewhat arbitrary. It is the combination of selected variables that gives a model its predictive power, and not any one variable in isolation.

The results suggest that access to GPs and private inpatient services are positively related to utilization, while the provision of nursing home places serves to depress NHS inpatient use. NHS inpatient provision was not found to affect utilization significantly. However, the need to include the density variable suggests that there are aspects of supply that are not being captured in the existing supply measures. Five variables clearly related to health care needs are included in the equation. The inclusion of SMR for ages 0 to 74 is in line with current resource allocation practice. The OLDALONE and S_CARER variables suggest influences on utilization caused by the level of support at home. The need to include UNEMP and MANUAL variables confirms a widely held belief that unemployment and social class are important determinants of health care needs which are not captured by SMR.

In the long stay specialties, difficulty was encountered in identifying a satisfactory model of estimated costs, even when lengths of stay for all long episodes were truncated to one year. As a result, the model presented here is of standard costs, for which the statistical specification was more satisfactory. Over the study period, many authorities were discharging more patients than they were admitting in the long stay specialties. The system was therefore not in a steady state, and the results should be viewed with more caution than those for the acute sector. Nevertheless, we believe that they represent the best available model of long stay utilization.

The variables included in a parsimonious model are as follows:

ACCNHSN	Access to NHS non-acute beds
ACCGPS	Access to general practitioners
HOMES*	Proportion of population aged 75+ not in nursing or residential homes

ACCPRI	Access to private hospital beds
PRIVRENT	Proportion in households in private rented accommodation
75+ALONE	Proportion aged 75+ living alone
PERMSICK	Proportion of adult population permanently sick
SMR074	Standardized mortality ratio (SMR) for ages 0–74

By far the most important needs variable in this model is PERMSICK. The PRIVRENT variable has a negative sign, suggesting that more private rented accommodation is associated with less utilization. As we shall show below, we suspect that PRIVRENT reflects some aspects of supply which our four supply variables have not captured, and we do not believe that there is a causal link between PRIVRENT and health care needs.

Towards a Formula

The final stage in the analysis was to use the models to derive a formula for distributing funds to health authorities. Although the results outlined in the previous section represent satisfactory statistical models of utilization, they are not directly useful for developing a resource allocation formula because they contain supply terms which may or may not reflect 'legitimate' health care needs. For the purposes of developing a formula, the requirement was to develop a measure which we term 'normative utilization': that is, the level of utilization that would arise in an area if it adopted national utilization rates in line with its health care needs. Implicit in this definition is the assumption that the measure should be sensitive to an area's health care needs, but independent of its supply of health care facilities.

Two practical difficulties emerge in seeking to make the concept of normative utilization operational. First, it is necessary to identify measures of health care needs. And second, it is necessary to estimate the link between those measures and utilization.

The modelling process described above indicated this study's assessment of the most important health and socio-economic determinants of use of inpatient facilities over and above supply considerations. Therefore, in the absence of any other unambiguous indicators of health care needs, these were assumed to be the legitimate drivers of normative utilization.

In estimating the link between these needs variables and utilization, it is however important to note that they affect utilization in two ways: first through their direct impact on utilization, and second through their indirect influence on supply, which in turn influences utilization. That is, if in a schematic sense utilization U, needs N and supply S are linked by the equation

$$U = \alpha N + \beta S$$

then the impact of needs on utilization is given by the total derivative

$$\frac{dU}{dN} = \alpha + \beta \frac{\partial S}{\partial N}$$

These values are the coefficients of needs variables identified in an ordinary least squares regression of utilization on the unambiguous needs indicators identified above. The next stage in the analysis was therefore to carry out this regression, and to recommend the use of the resultant coefficients as the basis for a resource allocation formula.

Examination of the standardized coefficients in the acute sector model suggests that UNEMP is the most important determinant of normative utilization, and that OLDALONE, S_CARER and SMR074 are of roughly equal importance. MANUAL is less important than any of these variables. In the long stay sector by far the most important needs indicator of utilization is PERMSICK. Of the remaining three needs variables, only SMR074 remains statistically significant at the 5% level.

One important final consideration is that many of the supply influences on NHS inpatient utilization are likely to be the result of the administrative policies of DHAs and FHSAs. Modelling the effects of these policies in a small area study is complicated, because the supply effect operates at the same level on all the wards within an administrative area. To model this satisfactorily requires the use of multilevel modelling methodologies. The final stage of this study, not completed at the time of writing, will therefore be to subject the models described above to multilevel analysis, to determine whether coefficients change significantly if the multilevel nature of the supply effects is taken into account.

We have recommended to the Department of Health that results of the sort described above should form the basis of a formula for distributing HCHS funds to geographical areas. Clearly, other components of the formula need to be designed. For example, it is necessary to weight populations for age and sex. And the acute and long stay models must be combined in certain proportions, which might be determined by the existing split of expenditure between the two sectors. Moreover, decisions must be made about the extent to which these results are used to distribute revenue relating to non-inpatient services: specifically, outpatient and community services. However, we believe that the results given here can form the basis of a formula based on a sound underlying model, and good empirical evidence.

Conclusions

The study was undertaken over a four month period, using readily available data provided by the Department of Health. Clearly given more resources and a longer time scale it might have been possible to secure minor improvements to the models. In addition, the study team was acutely aware of the shortcomings of using utilization data as a proxy for health care needs. Nevertheless, within the limitations of data availability, we believe that this study has made optimal use of a small area analysis of utilization. Indeed, in a number of ways we believe that it marks an advance on previous work in modelling determinants of small area use of inpatient facilities.

The study team had available a more comprehensive dataset than previous researchers, including cost-based utilization data, four supply variables, and a wealth of up to date Census and other socio-economic data. The team sought to use statistical techniques appropriate to overcoming some of the empirical difficulties encountered in disentangling needs and supply determinants of utilization. And we believe that the interpretation of results marks an advance on previous work, in seeking to quantify the impact of needs on utilization both directly and, through supply, to the extent that it reflects needs. We therefore feel that the results of this study offer the best available basis for an equitable formula distributing HCHS funds.

References

Carr-Hill, R, Hardman G, Martin S, Peacock S, Sheldon T A and Smith P (1993). *A formula for distributing NHS revenues based on small area use of hospital beds*, in preparation.

Address for contact

Mr Peter Smith, Department of Economics and Related Studies, University of York, York, YO1 5DD.

Resource Allocation to Fundholding Practices

BRIAN JARMAN and MADHAVI BAJEKAL, Department of General Practice, St Mary's Hospital Medical School

From April 1991 the resources for hospital and community health services have been allocated to regions on the basis of a weighted capitation formula. A region's allocation is derived by applying a cost per head for seven age-groups (determined by the Department of Health) to the region's resident population distribution in those age groups. This allocation is then multiplied by a factor to allow for the level of illness in the region (the factor used is the square root of the regional standardised mortality ratio under the age of 75, $\sqrt{\text{SMR}}$ 75). Regions then allocate resources to districts – usually based on this formula with modifications to allow for social conditions in each district.

The funds for the fundholding procedures for residents in each district registered with fundholding practices are top-sliced from the district allocations. It is important that the way that funds are allocated to fundholding practices is similar to the way in which funds are allocated by regions to DHAs. Services for patients registered with non-fundholding practices are purchased by district purchasing authorities and there should be equality with fundholder patients. This will entail moving towards a weighted capitation formula for allocating funds for fundholding activity.

An additional advantage of weighted capitation allocations for fundholding practices is as a means of introducing equity in the resources available for treating patients within general practice. This approach could help to address one of the criticisms of fundholding practices, namely that they are less likely than district health authorities to target their services according to need for health service provision. A formula based on identified needs at a local level would highlight the 'needs' aspect of general practice service provision and provide a benchmark to assess current in-patient and out-patient activity of the residents of a locality.

This methodology could be applied to consortia of fundholding practices. Also, if practices were to be allowed to hold funds for a wider range of services than those currently included in fundholding, these could fairly easily be calculated. A capitation method for fundholder allocations could also be used to evaluate under or over spending of allocated fundholder funds at the year end.

In order to develop a model for general practice fundholder allocations it is now possible to use in-patient and out-patient data of reasonable quality which have been available for most regions from Hospital Activity records from about 1988 onwards. These can be used to build a model for fundholding practice allocations based on a methodology similar to that used in the RAWP Review (1988).

The data which are needed for fundholding studies are best collected in five different databases, linked by a common geographical level of aggregation – namely the 1981 or 1991 census wards. For years other than 1981 or 1991 census years postcoded data can be extracted and then allocated to their 1981 or 1991 census defined electoral ward. This link between a postcode current in any particular year and its 1981 or 1991 ward location may be made via the frozen postcode directory for the year in question. This procedure ensures that all the databases are aggregated to the same geographical boundaries for analysis irrespective of the large number of inter-census ward boundary changes.

The five linked databases are:

> Population
> Mortality
> Socio-economic indicators
> Bed availability and accessibility
> Hospital activity

The distribution of resident population at ward level is available only for the census year. For inter-census years, there are two potential sources for estimating the ward population and its distribution by age and sex – first, the annual OPCS population estimates available at district level and second, the FHSA patient registers. Because the size and structure of the population are key determinants of need for resources, both these sources should be used to estimate the ward populations.

The OPCS population estimates at district level can be distributed to the district's wards in the same ratio as the proportional distribution that existed in 1981 or 1991. In other words, changes in the constitutent ward's total population and its age/sex distribution are assumed to mirror the overall changes in the district population's age/sex counts with no additional correction for between-ward population shifts in the inter-census years.

Ward level population estimates are also derived by allocating the postcoded FHSA patient registers to electoral wards. While this method of estimating ward populations has the advantage of incorporating the actual ward population movements more precisely than census data, its main drawbacks are that the FHSA population registers are inflated by patients who have not been removed from the FHSA registers and also are affected by the small percentage of people (about 2% nationally) who are not registered with a general practitioner at all or who are still registered with a general practitioner whom they had when they were living at a previous address. The FHSA register provides the only source for the general practitioner practice populations and their geographic or ward spread, as well as their age/sex distribution, and therefore, although the OPCS populations may be used for modelling at ward level, the FHSA populations must be used for calculating the final predicted budgets for the practices.

Mortality

Given that the average numbers of deaths per ward annually are small (around 60), it is necessary to combine the mortality data for a number of years to calculate standardised mortality ratios. The aggregation of data over a number of years serves to minimise the impact of chance variability in the numbers of deaths. The degree of confidence that the ratios are an accurate summary measure of the mortality of the ward is statistically quantifiable in terms of the narrowness of the width of the confidence intervals.

Standardised Mortality Ratios (SMRs) are calculated for the time periods when hospital activity data are available. The postcoded mortality database for each year is first aggregated to ward level to provide the numbers of deaths by standard 10 year age-bands (ages <1, 1–4, 5–14 . . .85+) and sex. The expected mortality is calculated by applying the average national (England & Wales) age and sex-specific rates to the ward age and sex structure in the relevant time period. SMRs are calculated for all ages, for ages up to age 75 (SMR75), and ages up to age 65 (SMR65).

Socio-Economic Indicators

These are largely census-based indicators (available for 1981 and 1991). In addition to seven composite variables (such as the underprivileged area (UPA) score and the Townsend and Carstairs indices), there are about 50 single percentage variables which may be considered as possibly relevant in the analyses. Although the census provides a wide range of variables which can be used as measures of the social profile of each ward, their major drawback is that they may become considerably out-of-date several years after the census. However, the Department of Employment produces counts of the number of persons unemployed for every quarter (NOMIS data). These figures may be reallocated to 1981 or 1991 ward boundaries to produce a measure of unemployed males, females, and total persons as a percentage of the residents in the corresponding categories for each ward.

Bed Availability and Accessibility

A bed availability factor may be calculated for each DHA and the wards within the DHA ascribed this value. The bed availability factor may be computed in two steps. First, for each DHA the number of acute beds available per thousand population is calculated. Then the weighted mean bed availability score of each district is calculated using a weighting for the central district and a lower weighting for other districts. The weighting for other districts may be in proportion to the patient flow to that district. This method does not work well for districts which have Special Health Authorities.

Other bed supply variables based on the distance of wards from hospitals and the numbers of beds available in each hospital have also been developed.

Hospital Activity

All acute plus geriatrics consultant episodes and fundholding chargeable consultant episodes can be extracted from the postcoded Hospital Activity data. The Mersey datasets are used to adjust for cross boundary flows and then individually aggregated to ward. The extracted fundholding chargeable episodes usually include elective admissions and day cases after excluding private patients. The ward-aggregated data constitute the actual number of cases and total number of bed-days for both acute plus geriatrics episodes and for fundholding chargeable episodes. The bed-days are subsequently converted to average beds used daily.

Activity rates for both numbers of episodes and average beds used daily for acute plus geriatrics episodes and fundholding episodes by 10 year age groups and sex are calculated. The regional rates may be used in the calculation of standardised acute plus geriatrics episodes, fundholding consultant episodes and average beds used daily.

Cost Calculations

In addition to the ward-level databases, costs per head for fundholding in-patient consultant episodes and out-patient attendances must be calculated. In order to provide target budgets, costs per head for seven age groups as defined in the Department of Health weighted capitation formula may be used. Expenditure by seven age groups for fundholding activity can be used to work out an average cost per head for each age group. There are problems when the costs of the hospital services available to each practice differ greatly and these have not been clearly resolved. If a region uses a fixed cost per age group, then practices which normally use hospitals which are relatively expensive are disadvantaged. This problem can be particularly serious if the provider hospitals which are available have unavoidable costs, related for example to teaching, which are not adequately allowed for at the hospital end.

The Model

Past research on the variation in hospital utilisation has shown that usage varies with respect to a number of factors which operate simultaneously. Following the underlying concepts and hypotheses contained in the 1988 RAWP Review, we have viewed usage as a function of varying availability or supply of services and of varying relative need for services. In order to achieve equity in allocation, one of the fundamental principles of resource allocation has been that resources should be allocated according to need with no account taken of above or below average levels of supply of services. An empirical estimate of the relative need for services, after allowing for varying supply, can be made by modelling factors known to be associated with levels of use. The regression coefficients of each of the independent or explanatory variables in the model selected provide an estimate of the strengths of their corresponding effects on utilisation.

The form of the standardised model chosen could be of two types – additive or multiplicative. The additive model is of the type:

Standardised Fund Holding Consultant Episodes
= constant + a*(bed availability) + b*(health factor) + c*(social factor)

The additive model implies that each factor separately adds to the likelihood of admission. This assumption is intuitively less plausible than the multiplicative model which is based on the theory that each of these explanatory factors interact or contribute simultaneously to the probability of being admitted to hospital.

The standardised multiplicative model chosen therefore is of the form:

Standardised FHCE = constant *(bed availability)^a *(heath factor)^b *(social factor)^c

Logarithmic transformation (ln) of the multiplicative model yields an additive structure of the form below and the paramenters a, b and c can be estimated.

Ln (SFHCE) = ln (constant) + a*ln(bed availability) + b*ln(health factor) + c*ln(social factor)

Modelling Process

In view of the fact that the mortality measures are correlated with the measures of social status, the RAWP Review adopted a 2-stage approach to modelling. This approach allows the mortality variable to make its maximum contribution in explaining the variation of standardised hospital usage, allowing for the supply of hospital services but initially not including social factors. In this approach, the explanatory factors are modelled in stages. After each stage, the dependent variable is calculated as the ratio of the previous dependent or response variable to the value predicted by the first stage. The advantage of a staged approach is that the additional marginal effects of each factor can be quantified. However, when the factors are correlated, it should be noted that some of the explanatory power of the factors fitted in the second stage (such as social factors) are incorporated in the coefficient or effect of the first stage factor (mortality).

The coefficients for SMR75 (the best explanatory variable to use for health status) in the first stage of modelling has been found to be about 0.5, the value suggested by the RAWP Review. It is therefore convenient to make the ward formula correspond as closely as possible to the national weighted capitation formula and fix the coefficient of SMR75 to 0.5 for the next stage of modelling. In the second stage therefore, the dependent variable can be taken as the log of the ratio of the standardised hospital usage ratio to the square root of SMR75. In the second stage of modelling, unemployed as a percentage of total ward residents is a powerful explanatory social variable.

The model provides a method for calculating predicted budgets for individual practices. The steps involved in the calculation of the predicted budgets are first to use the cost per head in each age group multiplied by the numbers in the age bands to provide a total unadjusted cost per ward. This is then adjusted as discussed above for variations in levels of health, social conditions and bed supply. The total predicted budget for each practice is arrived at by summing over all the wards within which the practice's patients are distributed.

Alternatively, predicted fundholding activity for each practice can also be calculated by substituting cost per age group for average activity rates for each of the seven age groups. The total age-expected activity can then be adjusted for health and social factors to obtain predicted activity. The latter method provides a further dimension to the evaluation of practice activity in terms of numbers of fundholding episodes predicted and would be important particularly when there is a significant variation in provider unit costs.

Applying the Results

Our analysis for two regions has shown that after allowing for supply, the usage of fundholding type services is strongly related to the health needs of the resident populations, as measured by SMR under age 75, as well as socio-economic factors. There was a strong inverse relationship between standardised fundholding consultant episode ratio with social class I and II and a positive correlation with percent unemployed and composite indices of deprivation. The negative association with percent social classes I and II is possibly indicative of the use of private healthcare for elective surgery by these groups. However, the lack of data on private health provision and activity meant that this relationship could not be quantified or included as a term in the model. The count of benefit claimants by their ward of residence, from which we calculated the percent unemployed, provides the only annually updated socio-economic indicator available at ward level. Unemployment has been shown to be related to other measures of health service demand and utilisation. In the regions we studied, the variable percent unemployed was the socio-economic predictor which we used in the second stage of the model.

The standardised model explained 30% of the variation in chargeable hospital activity for the regions studied. When considering the overall explanatory power of the model, it should be borne in mind that the size and age structure of the population is the most important factor in the explanation of the variance contributing to about 88 to 90% of the variation. The addition of other explanatory factors increases the total R-square by a further 5% providing a maximum overall value of 95%. It is important to stress therefore that it is vital that the age-sex register of the practice at FHSA level be maintained as accurately as possible. In addition, some attempt should be made to examine critically the sources of error – list inflation as well as under-enumeration in areas with high transient populations – in the discrepancies between the district level mid-year population estimates, on which the district allocation is based, and the FHSA patient register.

At the end of the modelling process, we had determined the variables that best explain the variation in chargeable activity, after allowing for population structure and supply, and the relative strengths of their effects as measured by the coefficients or parameter estimates in the regression model. The latter therefore provide the weighting factors for adjusting the expected utilisation based on population distribution within a ward or a practice to give predicted activity. In the case of practices, as the population is spread over a number of wards, a scaled adjustment factor was calculated which took into account the proportion of patients of each practice resident in different wards and each ward's value for the adjusting variable.

Conclusion and Comments

As mentioned at the beginning of the paper, it is clear that as the population registered with fundholders increases, it will no longer be possible to set fundholder budgets on the basis of historic activity if equity between all purchasers is to be maintained. The second requirement of any proposed allocation strategy for chargeable activity is that it should be consistent with that used to allocate resources to districts for all services. The method we have adopted satisfies both these requirements and proposes a weighted capitation formula which takes into account the factors associated with the variation in the need for fundholder type services between different population groups (and hence practices) and is consistent, both in philosophy and application, with the national resource allocation formula.

On comparing allocations based on past activity with budgets predicted by our model, there was fairly good agreement. In cases where our capitation allocation differed significantly from historical activity allocations, our predictions were, in general, in agreement with the perceptions of the regions. The predicted budgets are primarily useful as benchmark figures for indicative targets but the pace at which districts move towards these would depend upon the implementation strategies of the regions.

Address for contact

Professor Brian Jarman, Department of General Practice, St Mary's Hospital Medical School, Lisson Grove Health Centre, Gateforth Street, London, NW8 8EG.

The Use of a Deprivation Index in Ireland: Initial Findings and Problems

ROSALEA WATTERS, Eastern Health Board, Ireland and CERI
PHILLIPS, Newport Business School

SUMMARY

The decisions surrounding health care resource allocation in Ireland
reveal a noticeable lack of rational criteria. Recent Government statements have indicated their intention to eliminate the inequalities which
exist in health and social services.

The aim of the study was to consider the implications of using an index
of deprivation, similar to that used in other countries, as the basis for
allocating resources between Community Care Areas within the Eastern
Health Board region. The indicators used to make up the Index were
based on the Jarman Underprivileged Area Score, the Townsend
Material Deprivation Score and the Scottish Deprivation Score, but
were selected to reflect the Irish situation. The Jarman methodology was
employed in aiming at a weighted index for each area. The budget was
then divided accordingly prior to comparison with the actual budget
allocation. Striking differences were revealed, ranging from a 97% loss
for one area to a 91% gain for another.

The study confirmed the need to develop a Deprivation Index as a basis
for allocating resources in Ireland. It also highlighted the limitations of
seeking to 'import' indicators or weightings from another country.
Lastly, the study gave direction to the way in which the model can be
moved forward to embrace Irish specifc factors.

Within the health services in Ireland, annual allocations are based largely on
incremental changes on the previous year's figures (O'Brien et al 1989). As in
virtually all other developed countries, demand for health care is outstripping
available resources and choices are having to be made. If, as stated by the
present Minister of Health (Howlin, 1993) the principles of equity, accountability and cost effectiveness are going to underlie all future planning in this
area, then it seems essential that the foundations upon which future services
are built are correctly laid. This would seem to require a fundamental change
in the actual method of resource allocation. The purpose of this study,
therefore, was to initiate the process of developing a Deprivation Index as one
possible way of achieving this.

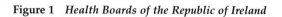

Figure 1   *Health Boards of the Republic of Ireland*

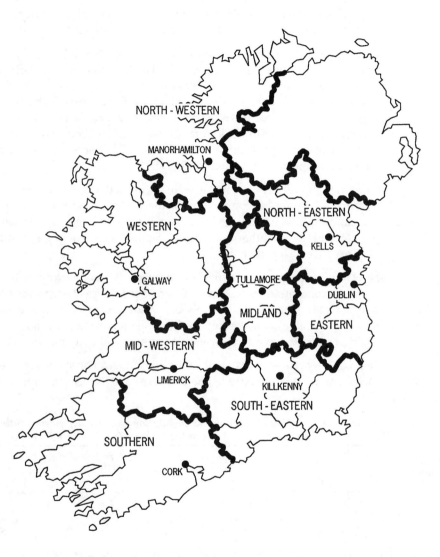

NORTH - WESTERN

MANORHAMILTON

WESTERN

NORTH - EASTERN

KELLS

GALWAY

TULLAMORE

DUBLIN

MIDLAND

EASTERN

MID - WESTERN

LIMERICK

KILLKENNY

SOUTH - EASTERN

SOUTHERN

CORK

The Republic of Ireland is, at present, divided into eight Health Boards (see Figure 1). Each Health Board functions under three distinct programmes:

1 **General Hospital Programme:** responsible for hospital services (excluding psychiatric), services for the physically handicapped and residential services for the elderly.
2 **Special Hospital Programme:** provides services for the mentally ill and mentally handicapped.
3 **Community Care Programme:** covers general practitioner, dental, community welfare and preventive health services.

Preventive health and social services are delivered through area units, known as Community Care Areas. The Eastern Health Board has the largest population in the country, covering Dublin City and County, Counties Wicklow and Kildare. It is divided into 10 Community Care Areas, Areas 9 and 10 being the largely rural counties of Kildare and Wicklow. Each area is made up of a variable number of District Electoral Divisions and is allocated a yearly budget for the delivery of preventive health and social services. Some services, and therefore budgets, are retained centrally.

Since the Community Care Areas were set up in the late seventies, with their resource allocation, the population of the Eastern Health Board has grown dramatically. This has resulted in the emergence of large new estates of both private and local authority housing. Significant demographic and social changes have also occurred.

How much the present system of resource allocation truly reflects these changes, concentrating resources where need is greatest, is therefore the central issue which this study set about considering. In the final analysis, it was hoped to be able to make initial recommendations around how resources could be allocated in a more scientific, rational and equitable manner.

Taking a very crude, overall look at the percentage of total budget received by each Community Care Area in one year (see Table 1), it would appear to have

Table 1   *Distribution of total budget, population and area dependency ratio for the 10 Community Care Areas of the Eastern Health Board (EHB)*

[Area]	% of Total Budget	% Pop EHB	Area Dependency Ratio*
1	7.5	9.9	53
2	11.9	9.3	45
3	6.99	7.0	52
4	10.1	12.1	63
5	7.7	8.4	63
6	12.3	11.1	57
7	12.6	9.7	53
8	12.1	15.3	59
9	10.1	9.5	57
10	8.9	7.7	68

*Dependency Ratio $= \dfrac{\text{Population under 15 + Population over 65}}{\text{Population between 15 + 65}} \times 100$

Total Pop EHB = 1,232,238   Dep Ratio of EHB = 58

no direct bearing on, or relationship with, the percentage of population or the Dependency Ratio (defined as the number of people under 15 years or over 65 years of age, divided by the number of people between 15 and 65 years), for that Area.

The Dependency Ratio alone was not considered a good basis for resource allocation as it is too narrow in its view and does not give a complete picture of an area's level of deprivation.

Development of Deprivation Index

In constructing the Deprivation Index, it seemed fair to use a combination of both direct and indirect indicators. In this way, some recognition would be given to situations which have the potential to be highly demanding on health and social services. It was also considered to be applicable to use a combination of social and material indicators. Given that no Irish Index was in existence, other indices were examined as a starting point for constructing an index applicable to the Irish situation. These indices were the Jarman Under-privileged Area Score (Jarman 1983, 1984), the Townsend Material Deprivation Score (Townsend et al, 1988) and the Scottish Deprivation Score (Carstairs and Morris, 1988). The Index constructed combined a number of the indicators used in these three indices.

The Jarman indicators which were *not* included were:
1   *Poor Housing:* In the past 20 years, the standard of housing in the Eastern Health Board region has greatly improved. It was therefore considered more applicable to use an indicator which gave a measure of overcrowding and thus a guide to living conditions.
2   *Ethnic Minorities:* The presence of a significant immigrant population has not, to date, been a major feature in Ireland. However, this situation is changing. Therefore, although excluded from this initial work, this indicator does merit consideration in the next stage.
3   *Single Parent Households:* This was not included as by itself it was not regarded as a deprived state. However, being a single parent and unemployed may present a different picture. Therefore, by using *total* unemployment figures, rather than male only, it was felt that this was somehow acting as proxy for single parent families.
4   *Highly Mobile People:* This indicator was excluded from this initial survey as figures were not readily available. However, it is acknowledged that high levels of mobility within an area cause increased demand on health and social services and therefore merit consideration. Ireland has quite a large population of 'Travellers' whose way of life is 'mobile.' Some way needs to be found to include this group within the Deprivation Index.
5   *Non-married Family Groups:* In the Irish context this was seen as not adding anything of significance to the overall picture of deprivation that was being constructed.

The Townsend indicators *not* used were:
1   *Economically Active Persons Seeking Work (Or temporarily sick):* total unemployment figures were used as proxy for this.

2   *Homes that are not Owner Occupied:* This was excluded as it was felt to add little to the measurement of deprivation in Ireland.

No Scottish indicators were excluded. In attempting to design a Deprivation Index for Ireland *total* unemployment figures were used. This would seem to reflect the situation more accurately than single sex, male only figures, as used in the Scottish Deprivation Score. Thus, this initial Irish Deprivation Index was a hybrid of the Jarman, Townsend and Scottish Indices, and is shown in Table 2. Unlike the Scottish Deprivation Score, demographic factors were included as it was considered that these, in combination with other indicators, contribute to a picture of overall deprivation in an area and thus to demand on health and social services.

Table 2   *Initial Irish Deprivation Index*

1	Percentage of population under 5 years of age.
2	Percentage of population over 75 years of age.
3	Percentage of population over 65 years and living alone.
4	Percentage of population in Social Class 5 and 6.
5	Percentage of population unemployed.
6	Average number of persons per room.
7	Average number of cars per household.

Results

Secondary census data was used to obtain figures for all of the indicators within each of the District Electoral Divisions. The information used was from the 1986 census, as all the figures were not available from the latest (1991) census.

As a preliminary step, it was decided to construct an Index for each of the ten Community Care Areas in order to compare suggested allocations (based on Deprivation Index) with actual resources allocated. The results of calculating the Deprivation Index for the Community Care Areas are shown in Table 3. This table shows the Deprivation Index for each area, the potential allocation of budget based on the Index and the actual percentage of total budget each area received in one specific year.

The question of whether or not the results should be weighted was considered. As no Irish weightings were available, those worked out by Jarman were used in this initial study, although the obvious drawbacks to this were recognised.

The results of applying the Jarman weightings to the indicators are shown in Table 4. The trends are similar to the unweighted results. However, this exercise mainly demonstrated the need to use weightings within context.

Table 3 *Deprivation index, potential and actual budget allocation for the 10 Community Care Areas of the Eastern Health Board. Unweighted results.*

[Area]	Deprivation Index (unweighted)	Potential Allocation % (unweighted)	Actual Allocation %
1	8.62	5.70	7.50
2	12.41	8.21	11.90
3	12.44	8.23	6.99
4	16.66	11.02	10.10
5	18.96	12.54	7.70
6	18.04	11.93	12.30
7	19.20	12.70	12.60
8	12.80	8.47	12.10
9	15.95	10.55	10.10
10	16.07	10.63	8.90

Table 4 *Deprivation index, potential and actual budget allocations for the 10 Community Care Areas of the Eastern Health Board. Weighted results.*

[Area]	Deprivation Index (weighted)	Potential Allocation % (weighted)	Actual Allocation %
1	0.35	0.23	7.50
2	7.71	4.96	11.90
3	12.51	8.05	6.99
4	18.11	11.65	10.10
5	22.81	14.68	7.70
6	20.90	13.44	12.30
7	24.64	15.85	12.60
8	6.96	4.48	12.10
9	22.60	14.54	10.10
10	18.85	12.12	8.90

Conclusions and Recommendations

This study set about looking at the present system of funding and considering an alternative approach. This approach was based on a series of indicators which were seen as a measure of the level of deprivation in specific areas.

The index used was constructed from a combination of demographic, social and material indicators. Seven indicators were used in the construction of the present index and the results suggest that there is merit in pursuing this concept. However, this paper only represents the early steps of the development of a Deprivation Index which could be used in Ireland as a basis for resource allocation. Other indicators which deserve consideration are the presence of ethnic minorities and highly mobile groups. Further consideration also needs to be given to ensure an adequate urban/rural mix.

The difference in the Index when using non-weighted and weighted indicators has been shown. However, if weightings are to be used, these must be calculated for the Irish situation.

One of the difficulties with using such an index is that, if based on census data, it is always out of date. In Ireland, the General Medical Service is means tested. Working on the principle that multiple deprivation is usually associated with low income (Townsend, 1987), it would be interesting to compare the result of the index as developed, with an index derived simply from the percentage covered by the GMS. If this seemed in line, then using this one indicator to construct the Deprivation Index would be simpler and could also be revised on a more frequent basis. The use of unemployment rates as a single indicator for deprivation has been suggested (Campbell et al, 1991) and certainly merits further work in Ireland, given the high levels of unemployment. This raises the question of whether one single indicator can adequately act as a measure of deprivation in its full conceptualisation.

In conclusion therefore, this paper has considered one possible means of achieving a more equitable system of resource allocation in Ireland. Only the initial stages are reported. If the potential of using a Deprivation Index is to be fully evaluated, then the index itself needs to be further developed. Weightings which are Irish based should be calculated. However, in the consideration of the basic quest, that is for a more equitable system, other methods also merit examination.

References

Campbell, D, Radford, J & Burton, P (1991). 'Unemployment rates: an alternative to the Jarman index?' *British Medical Journal* Vol 303: 750–755.

Carstairs, V & Morris, R (1989). 'Deprivation, mortality and resource allocation' *Community Medicine* Vol 11, No 4: 364–372.

Howlin, B (1992). Transcript of address delivered to the Association of Health Boards.

Jarman, B (1983). 'Identification of Underprivileged Areas.' *British Medical Journal* Vol 286, 1705–1709.

Jarman, B (1984). 'Under-privileged areas: validation and distribution' *British Medical Journal* Vol 289: 1587–1592

O'Brien et al (1989). *Report of the Commission on Health Funding* Dublin: published by the Stationery Office.

Townsend, P. (1987). 'Deprivation' *Journal of Social Policy* Vol 16; 124–146.

Townsend, P, Phillimore P and Beatrie, A (1988). 'Health and Deprivation: Inequality and the North.* Croom Helm, London.

Address for contact

Dr Rosalea Watters, Eastern Health Board, Community Care Office, Old County Rd, Crumlin, Dublin 12.

Is Use of Hospital Services a Proxy for Morbidity?

P C MILNER, J N PAYNE, S PATTERSON and J COY, Department of
Public Health, Rotherham Health Authority

ABSTRACT

Objectives

To examine the relationship between specific areas of morbidity measured
using validated survey questions and hospital service use and mortality to see
if the latter two could act as a proxy in health needs assessment, health service
planning, and resource allocation in a typical health district.

Design

A postal questionnaire was used to provide information about depression,
digestive disorders, musculo-skeletal disorders, obesity, respiratory disease,
and hip and knee pain. The questions were from survey instruments that have
been well validated and widely used to derive information about these
conditions, for example, the MRC Respiratory Questionnaire and Hospital
Anxiety and Depression Scale. The questionnaire was designed so that
questions could be considered in simple consecutive order and easily completed on four A4 pages. Envelopes and letters were addressed to named
people on health authority paper and sent out so that they could be completed
over the weekend. A reply-paid envelope was used for the first mailing and a
stamped addressed envelope for the reminder. Press releases were sent to all
local media, Members of Parliament, General Practitioners and Local
Councillors.

Hospital admissions were measured by finished consultant episodes for the
financial years 1987/8 to 1991/2. Relevant mortality data were obtained from
OPCS death tapes for the same period. Ward populations were based on the
1991 OPCS population estimates. The relationship between the prevalence of
these specific areas of morbidity and appropriate admission and mortality
rates were explored using linear regression and Pearson correlation analysis.

Setting

The population of Rotherham health district (255,000).

Subjects

A simple random sample of the residents of each of the 22 electoral wards in Rotherham health district identified from the electoral roll.

Results

Responses were obtained from 78% of the 5,000 sampled (82% after excluding people who had moved house or died). The morbidity prevalence for Rotherham were: depression 16%, digestive disease 36%, muscular-skeletal disorders 44%, obesity 10%, respiratory disease 28%, hip pain 10% and knee pain 24%. Significant, positive correlations were found between the prevalence of respiratory disease and the admission and mortality rates for respiratory problems (r = + 0.68, p <0.01 and r = 0.54, p <0.01), and the prevalence of depression and the admission rate for depression (r = + 0.52, p <0.05). No such relations were found for depression, digestive disease, musculo-skeletal disease, and obesity. For the conditions examined here, service use was a more useful measure than mortality.

Conclusions

Only two diseases (respiratory disease and depression) out of the seven diseases or procedures investigated had a positive correlation between hospital admission and disease prevalence. But even for these two the correlations explained less than 50% of the variance. Caution must be shown when service use is being considered as a proxy for morbidity.

Note:
This paper has been accepted for publication in the following journal. The abstract is reproduced here by kind permission of the editor of J Epidemiology & Community Health

Payne J N, Patterson S, Coy J, Milner P C. Is use of hospital services a proxy for morbidity? Journal of Epidemiology and Community Health; 1994: 48(1)

Address for contact

Dr Philip Milner, Director of Public Health, Department of Public Health, Rotherham Health Authority, Oakwood Hall Annexe, Moorgate Road, Rotherham, S60 2UN.

Stability and Equity in Resource Allocation to Purchaser Territories and GP Fundholders. A Review of the Mersey: 'Costed Strategy Approach'

R DEWHURST, F GILLET, T HENNELL and D KNIGHT, Mersey
Regional Health Authority

SUMMARY

Since 1989, ie before the introduction of the National NHS Internal
Market, the constituent health authorities in Mersey have been calculating target resource shares using an approach called 'The Costed Strategy'. The basic principles underlying this from the beginning have
been:

> Resident population (purchaser) based

> Calibrated using small area zones (electoral wards)

> Calculated by projecting target activity for a population, which is
> translated into resource shares using standard costs

The 1991 Census has allowed us to revisit some of the decisions made in
developing the general design of the approach – and to evaluate
possible alternative methods of doing the same job.

Key issues are:

> Stability: How stable year-on-year are the calibrated values on
> which the shares are based – and how consistent are the resulting
> purchaser shares?

> Updatability: How far does the spatial pattern of sub-regional
> population characteristics show consistent change over time, and
> does this imply annual updating of calibrations?

> Accessibility and Provider Practice: Is it appropriate to allow for
> these effects, and how can it be done?

> The Nature of Health Needs applied to a local population. How
> this is understood crucially affects the construction of an allocation
> formula.

Fundholder Issues

Fundholders receive budget allocations calculated from historic activity at current provider prices. As a purchaser territory undergoes strategic shift to adjust its allocation towards a target revenue share: so the fundholder budgets covering its population may cease to be compatible with resources available to non-fundholders. If as a consequence, fundholder budgets are controlled against capitation targets (set using standard costs), they will then no longer be compatible with purchaser–provider contracts.

It follows that the method of allocating resources to practice populations in respect of services within fundholding definitions should be broadly comparable – irrespective of whether the population concerned is registered with a Fundholder or not.

1   Introduction

Many studies have used small area geography to explore the association between hospital usage and population characteristics. Debate has centred on the *form* of model used, and on the choice of *explanatory* variables. We believe that the design of a stable and equitable allocation method is much more sensitive to the specification of the *usage* variables. We see the global phenomenon that is hospital usage as being an aggregation of a multiplicity of condition-specific relationships which cannot be assumed to be interdependent. We have therefore sought to separate dissimilar cases, while grouping similar ones on the basis of significant association with morbidity/deprivation indicators, following standardisation for age and sex. To that end, we have kept the explanatory model simple, but applied it differentially to distinct aggregations of caseload.

2   Basic principles

If purchasers are devoting their time and skills to questioning the calculation of their allocations – then the allocation approach is failing. The allocations must inspire confidence – which in turn depends on their being demonstrably stable and equitable. Neither goal is easy to achieve.

Stability – the chief cause of instability is uncertainty over size of purchaser populations. These problems are only compounded if allocation models use explanatory variables whose year-on-year variation is likely to be high (Figure 1).

Equity – allocation weightings that were equitable when the methodology was calibrated may become inequitable over time. Particular attention must be paid to the differential effects of changes in health care practice; and also to the changes in the characteristics of a purchaser's resident population due to migration.

Figure 1 *Stability of Social Variables in MRHA*

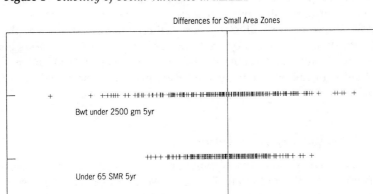

Differences for Small Area Zones

Bwt under 2500 gm 5yr

Under 65 SMR 5yr

% unemployed 1yr

% illegitimate 5yr

-1.6   -1.2   -0.8   -0.4   0   0.4   0.8   1.2

Current minus Previous Year (Z score)

3 The 'costed strategy' approach 1987–1991

This method has been used for allocation targets in Mersey since 1989. As originally formulated, it was assumed that utilisation (hospital admissions and length of stay) varied with age and sex (births for Maternity). We expected that certain categories of utilisation would require further adjustment for differences in socio-economic status, morbidity and supply. These adjustments were to be calibrated from an analysis of electoral ward resident populations using stepwise multiple regression. Well babies were excluded.

We rejected 1981 Census variables as outdated. This limited our choice to what was available. We settled for:

log(n)Unemployment(12 monthly),
<65 SMR(5 year), and
Specialty Beds/(1,000 pop within 5 miles).

Age-banded populations for electoral wards were calculated by adjusting 1981 counts to mid-year estimates and projections for Local Authority Districts.

Our pilot studies showed a high inter-correlation between morbidity and socio-economic indicators. We also found that the difference in population size between electoral wards in Cheshire and those in Merseyside gave rise to a strongly bimodal distribution – creating spurious linear relationships. We clustered contiguous wards with similar characteristics in Cheshire to eliminate this.

51

To eliminate the inter-correlations, we used the technique of principal components to orthogonalise our explanatory variables. To do this we forced the FACTOR procedure in SPSS to generate three components – where the default specification will have produced only one. The components thus generated are, by definition, Z scores (scaled with a mean of zero and a standard deviation of 1.0). Hence the variables are generally unaffected by changes in administrative definition (eg unemployment counts).

4   Caseload aggregations

Elective and non-elective admissions were kept separate – except in Maternity/SCBU and Mental Illness. We allocated cases by specialty of admission to 12 specialty groups (Mental Handicap was not analysed). For Medicine, General Surgery, Orthopaedics and Mental Illness; cases were separated into Child, Adult and Elderly age-bands. Medical cases over 65 and staying longer than 50 days were classified as Continuing Care (for data see Appendix).

Non-elective admissions proved to be correlated with our explanatory variables (Rsq>0.20), except in Ophthalmology, Maternity/SCBU and Radiotherapy. Correlations for elective caseloads, though statistically significant, always explained less than 20% of the residual variance. We tested caseloads for 87/88, 88/89 & 89/90. Specialty coefficients were stable for non-elective cases, but unstable for elective cases. We confined allocation adjustments to non-elective categories.

Both admissions and length of stay proved to be significantly associated with our morbidity and deprivation variables for total caseloads – but the sub-aggregations specified above eliminated the associations with length of stay. It appears that the longer average length of stay for residents in high-needs areas, arises from their greater proportion of non-elective admissions.

The model as specified generates expected admissions and bed days used by specialty, the coefficients on the 'supply' components not being used. These we translated into proportional revenue target shares using standard costs. In 1990 we re-calibrated utilisation rates using episodes rather than admissions – in order to be consistent with national caseload definitions and hospital costing returns. We also reduced the threshold for Continuing Care to 40 days.

5   Review of costed strategy – 1991 Census

In 1992 the decision was made to review the methodology. The development of GP Fundholding brought into question whether the movement of purchasers to their target allocations would be achievable. This was further complicated as purchaser districts established Locality Purchasing Initiatives for groups of non-fundholders.

The 1991 Census generated small area populations which would (we hoped) give us more robust estimates for our population denominators. We expected to use the census question on limiting illness; and we also found that the census data on residents over 75 in Nursing/Residential Homes allowed us to test the effects of non NHS provision. We were provided with the complete set of National Specialty Cost Returns (FR22), and were able to commission from the East Cheshire Statistical Analysis Consultancy a regression analysis distinguishing specialty-specific bed-day and episode costs (Johnson 1993). These we used as standard case costs. We did not have small area data for outpatient attendances; we therefore calculated average total outpatient spend divided by finished consultant episodes, and added this cost to the episode element of our specialty costing model.

6 Single needs variable

We revisited our approach to establishing morbidity and deprivation principal components. In doing so we found that the year-on-year values of principal component variables were unstable at a small area level. As a trial exercise, we attempted to apply the most recent version of our model to data from the North Western Region and found it did not fit the data supplied. Furthermore, when we analysed the Limiting Long-standing Illness question from the 1991 Census, we found that small area values correlated more strongly with log(n)Unemployment than they did with the Standardised Mortality Rate. We concluded that the indicators available to us would not allow a robust distinction to be drawn between morbidity and deprivation effects.

The basic form of the equation of interest was restated so that utilisation (age/ sex standardised) would be a function of Needs, Bed Supply, GP Supply and Percentage 75+ in communal homes. The GP supply variable was the same as the Bed Supply – but calculated for a 3 mile radius. The regressions would be weighted by zonal population. We identified about 30 possible needs input variables from the Census and Birth & Death Registration data. These were fed into a series of stepwise multiple regressions against utilisation rates. Seven variables emerged from this sifting process as having significant associations with caseload (Table 1).

A principal component analysis was run on the seven variables (only one factor being generated) – and the resulting component values regressed against caseloads. Then input variables were removed in turn, and the regressions rerun. Eventually, the seven were reduced to four – such that the explanatory power of the component would be reduced if any variable were to be added, any to be exchanged, or any to be subtracted. It was clear, however, that the illegitimacy variable was unsuited to model cases over 65 years of age.

Table 1 *Starting Variables from Stepwise Analysis*

% Permanent Sickness – persons of Working Age

% Unemployment

% Households without a car

% Children in Non-earning households

% Births – lone parent illegitimacy (3 year)

% Households with Dependents

Standardised Limiting Illness in Households

Standardised Mortality 0–74 (3 year)

Figure 2

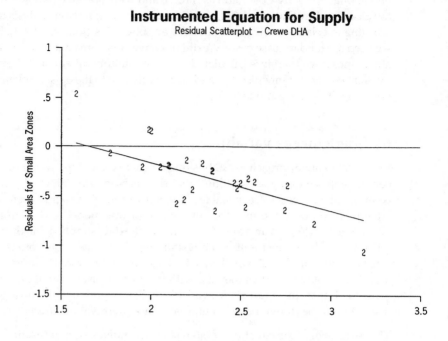

Instrumented Equation for Supply
Residual Scatterplot – Crewe DHA

Predicted : Beds/1000/(d+16km)sq
——— Regional Regression

Instrumented Equation for Supply
Residual Plot for District Catchments

Predicted : Beds/(1000/(d+16km)sq)
——— Regional Regression

We therefore split the input variable set into two and generated two explanatory components for each zone. In practice the resulting component values could be approximated almost exactly by converting the Input variables for each zone into Z scores, and then adding them across (ie the factor scores for the input variables turn out to be nearly equal).

Persons 0–64

Persons 65+

log(n)% male unemployment (DOE count)
log(n)% lone parent illegitimacy
SIR in households 0–64
SMR 0–64

log(n)% male unemployment (DOE count)
SIR in households 65+
SMR 65–74

7 Simultaneity of supply and utilisation

Recent studies have suggested that the coefficients of an Ordinary Least Squares (OLS) analysis for hospital caseloads might be biased due to the simultaneity of utilisation and supply. It is assumed that utilisation may be a function of supply – but it is clear that supply is (in part at least) a function of previous utilisation. Approaches suggested to remedy this apparent analytical solecism include Two-staged Least Squares (TSLS) regression (Johnston 1972) and this we attempted to implement. We found, however, that we could not construct a first stage (supply) equation that satisfied the formal requirements of linear regression – as the residuals from this equation were clearly related to the predicted supply values (Figure 2).

This led us to suggest that studies using the TSLS approach have misstated the form of the supply relationship. It has been assumed that supply (S) is a function of (lagged) needs (N) and utilisation(U):

$$Sc = F(Nc, Uc) - \text{for area c.} \quad \textbf{(1)}$$

But this applies only for a hospital catchment area. For a small zone (z) within the catchment area the relationship is given by:

$$Szc = f1(Nc, Uc), f2(\text{distance z to h}) - \text{for zone z.} \quad \textbf{(2)}$$

Hence the supply accessible to a zone does not depend solely on utilisation by the residents of that zone – but on the average utilisation of the catchment area as a whole. This suggests that such simultaneity as may be present would not be catastrophic – and that OLS regressions should give acceptable results.

8 Results

The results are given in Table 2. They are broadly consistent with those for the original, three component, model except that elective gynaecology now emerges as correlated with the needs variable. Comparisons with previous caseload sets showed this to be due to the general redefinition of colposcopy as an outpatient, rather than a day case procedure. As before, we only used those coefficients where the Rsq value exceeds 0.20. Given the number of zones observed, most relationships (however weak) will appear significant on one year's data or another. We consider that considerations of stability imply a rather more rigorous hurdle for inclusion in an allocation model.

Table 2 *Results from Regression Analysis*
Coefficients for Principal Component Variables

Specialty	Age	Non-elective		Elective	
		Coeff.	Rsq	Coeff.	Rsq
Medical	0–14	.20597	8%		
	15–64	.38447	78%	.1119	10%
	65+	.22991	65%	.1324	8%
C Care	65+	.25502	63%	.0985	6%
Surgery	0–14	.16703	26%	.0725	9%
	15–64	.22506	59%	.0827	15%
	65+	.12981	22%		
ENT	all age	.13132	11%	.1283	14%
T&O	0–14	.21304	35%		
	15–64	.21504	51%	.0554	13%
	65+	.14681	19%	−.103	9%
Dental	all age	.24391	25%	−.1296	12%
Ophthalmology	all age	.09037	3%	.1045	14%
Gynaecology	all age	.16777	36%	.1236	31%
Maternity	15–64				
SCBU	0–14				
Radiotherapy	all age				
MI	15–64	.35938	55%		

9   Fundholder procedures

All fundholder procedures are, by definition, elective. The Mersey Region has developed a price banding categorisation for Fundholder procedures. We tested individual price bands for association with the needs component variable. Five price bands were found to have significant associations (Table 3). The Rsq values for Ophthalmology cases were below our 0.20 threshold – but Gynae(B), Thoracic(A) and Surgery(AA) were all strongly significant.

We then focused on individual procedures within the price band. In Gynaecology, the strong association was found to be due to sterilisations, while that for thoracic medicine was due to bronchoscopies. Neither of these is a surprising result. What was surprising, was that the strong needs association in Surgery(AA) arose entirely from Gastroscopies. No other fundholder procedure within the Surgical category shows a strong needs association.

The answer to the conundrum appears to be provided by the analysis of diagnoses following a gastroscopy. Only 2% of investigations (those that reveal cancer) have a necessary sequel in hospital treatment (Figure 3). The remainder are providing reports back to the GP to enable ulcer treatment drugs to be directed to the patient's specific condition. Since these drugs represent 10% of prescribing by value, it follows that gastroscopy, while of peripheral signifi-

Table 3 *GP Fundholder Procedures correlated with Needs Variable*
Mersey Region Zones 1991/92

	Correlations	Rsq
General Surgery		
100AA	.5817**	34%
GASTROSCOPY	.5743**	33%
COLONOSCOPY	.2338**	5%
SKIN BIOPSY	.2919**	9%
SIGMOIDOSCOPY	.1456	2%
OTHER SURGERY AA	.2961**	9%
100A	.2199**	5%
100B	.1015	1%
100C	.1243	2%
Urology		
101AA	.1032	1%
101A	.1217	1%
101B	.0717	1%
Orthopaedics		
110A	.2908**	8%
110B	−.0043	0%
110C	−.1775*	3%
ENT Surgery		
120A	.1249	2%
120B	.3354**	11%
120C	.2396**	6%
Ophthalmology		
130A	.3607**	13%
130B	.3959**	16%
Cardiothoracic		
170A	.5626**	32%
170B	.1257	2%
170C	.1440	2%
340B	.2105**	4%
340C	.2147**	5%
Gynaecology		
502AA	−.1770*	3%
502A	.2934**	9%
502B	.5830**	34%
STERILISATION	.5516**	30%
OTHER GYNAECOLOGY	.2654**	7%
502C	.0891	1%

cance in hospital treatment, is central to the proper functioning of general practice medicine – and of key importance in controlling national prescribing costs.

Gastroscopy and its consequential treatment represent less than 0.4% of acute hospital costs – but it is by far the most common elective treatment carried out in hospital, representing about 8% of all elective episodes, and 11% of

Figure 3 *Elective Gastroscopy in Mersey, 1991/92*
Principal Diagnosis of 15,315 Procedures

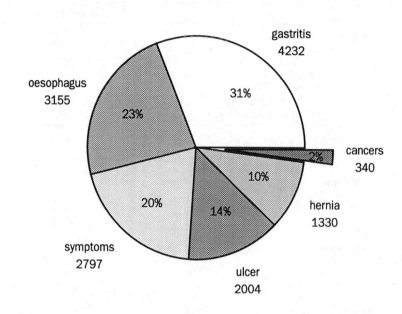

fundholding procedures. Analysis of gastroscopy in Mersey shows no consistent pattern for specialty of admission – some hospitals carry out all elective gastroscopies under the care of a surgeon – a rather greater number categorise them all as general medical cases. In many units the specialty designation appears to be random. This presumably reflects the loose association between this procedure and the rest of the hospital's activity.

Two points follow from this:
a. That an analysis of elective utilisation that fails to extract gastroscopy into a distinct category is likely to give misleading results in small area analysis.
b. That GP fundholder allocations (and contracts) should treat gastroscopy as a procedure – not differentiated by specialty. It should be noted that most of the procedures in the Surgery(AA) band also exhibit wide variation in specialty of admission.

10   Conclusions – Provider and Purchaser issues

The data used to calibrate an allocation formula are derived from provider's operational systems – activity and costs. Of necessity these are categorised into dimensions that suit the management agenda of providers, in particular in enabling units to establish departmental management budgets for cost centres. An allocation formula must recognise these limitations – but should also take account of the different agenda of purchasers, and ensure that the activity and cost categorisation used is consistent with purchasers' objectives.

Issues that require to be addressed.

a   **Episodes – Admissions.** Cost information is generated for episodes, whereas resident utilisation is better measured using admissions.

b **Specialties – Conditions.** We have already noted the loose specialty designation of several low-cost/high-volume procedures.

c **Elective/Non-elective Admissions.** While this is coded by the provider; it represents a key purchaser dimension – especially for fundholders. Our work shows that aggregation within these categories distinguishes a fundamental difference in health needs and their relation to hospital treatment.

d **The District Purchaser.** The services left once GP fundholder budgets have been set are widely different in scope and nature. Parts – immediate admissions, maternity – cover the whole population; other parts only cover non-fundholders. To make sense of this it is desirable that the institutional purchaser is allocated a budget for fundholder services on the same basis as the fundholders. The same principle ought to apply to fundholder weighted capitation. For the provider this implies that prices quoted for fundholding procedures ought to be used in contracts for all persons whether fundholder registered or not.

11   The way forward

The Census has allowed a rebasing of much of the analytical work that has been done on health needs and resource use. We see particular priorities for further work.

Community Services. We are looking at individual contact data supplied by a selection of Community Providers.

Priority Services. We are collecting care-group data on current contract spend. This will inform Purchasers in determining the particular elements of their service provision that is over/under target. It may also permit protection of priority service elements within the target formulae.

Provider Costs. Current contract prices are not consistent across purchasers – and hence add hidden subsidies/overheads onto current purchaser resource shares.

Census Adjustments. The Census is known to have missed about a million people – mainly young adults and predominantly male (Diamond 1993). This means that the population denominators from the census are unreliable, and that particular social variables (eg youth unemployment, overcrowding) are so biased as to be usable only with extreme care. Fortunately, the Long-term Illness question is likely to be only minimally affected (Simpson 1993). If Census variables are to be used for allocations to local purchasers then they may require updating for known population changes. It is possible that these issues can be addressed using the Sample of Anonymised Records (Williamson 1993).

Additional Data – JUVOS unemployment. Once the 1991 Census travel-to-work data has been analysed to determine homogeneous labour market areas, the DOE unemployment benefit claimant count will be recalculated on the 1991 ward geography (expected very soon). These figures are updated annually – and are probably a better indicator of socio-economic status than is the census count (Green 1993). We have been able for Mersey to adjust the data to the 1991 geography manually.

References

Diamond I (1993). Who and where are the 'missing million'. – presented at Conference 'Research on the 1991 Census'.*

Green A (1993). Alternative Measures of Unemployment. – presented at Conference 'Research on the 1991 Census'.*

Johnson K (1993). Analysis of 1991/92 Specialty Costs. East Cheshire Statistical Analysis Consultancy.

Johnston J (1972). Econometric Methods. McGraw-Hill. Chapters 12 & 13 pp 341–423.

Simpson S (1993). Measuring and coping with local under-enumeration in the 1991 Census. – presented at Conference 'Research on the 1991 Census'.*

Williamson P, Birkin M & Rees P (1993). The simulation of whole populations using data from the small area statistics, samples of anonymised records and national surveys. – presented at Conference 'Research on the 1991 Census'.*

*Abstracts of the papers from the 1993 Conference have been published with summaries of discussions in:

> Champion A G & Rees P H (1993). Research on the 1991 Census, Conference held at the University of Newcastle upon Tyne, 13–15 September 1993: – A Report. Working Paper 93/21, School of Geography, University of Leeds.

Address for contact

Mr Tom Hennell, Mersey Regional Health Authority, Hamilton House, 24 Pall Mall, Liverpool, L3 6AL.

Appendix: Table i

Episodes/10,000	Hospitalisation Rates 1991/2						
	0–4	5–14	15–44	45–64	65–74	75–84	85+
Male Non-elective							
Medicine and Paediatrics	1,165	206	234	620	1,343	2,397	3,587
Elderly Continuing Care	0	0	0	0	78	194	410
Surgical Specialties	148	132	144	188	393	656	990
ENT Surgery	13	9	11	12	20	28	19
Orthopaedics and Trauma	54	104	73	54	68	126	251
Ophthalmology	3	5	5	8	13	25	22
Dental and Oral Surgery	3	3	8	2	2	2	3
Radiotherapy	0	0	1	6	12	12	3
Mental Illness	4	8	64	52	63	155	221
Female Non-elective							
Medicine and Paediatrics	876	174	218	427	929	1,732	2,608
Elderly Continuing Care	0	0	0	0	58	178	336
Surgical Specialties	83	87	114	135	196	288	395
ENT Surgery	14	9	8	9	13	16	15
Orthopaedics and Trauma	42	60	27	47	106	244	465
Ophthalmology	3	2	2	5	12	26	31
Dental and Oral Surgery	2	1	2	1	1	1	2
Gynaecology	1	3	216	28	18	21	16
Radiotherapy	0	0	1	7	7	5	2
Mental Illness	0	1	50	58	88	169	233
Male Elective							
Medicine and Paediatrics	84	61	108	291	427	431	309
Elderly Continuing Care	0	0	0	0	4	8	13
Surgical Specialties	242	138	225	516	999	1,108	785
ENT Surgery	185	173	53	54	57	45	23
Orthopaedics and Trauma	22	35	108	127	120	109	55
Ophthalmology	39	15	14	51	160	282	368
Dental and Oral Surgery	16	38	43	17	15	17	12
Maternity/SCBU	343	0	0	0	0	0	0
Radiotherapy	1	0	5	15	34	35	39
Female Elective							
Medicine and Paediatrics	66	70	96	231	322	265	273
Elderly Continuing Care	0	0	0	0	4	8	11
Surgical Specialties	68	52	204	420	469	421	255
ENT Surgery	108	183	50	37	29	22	12
Orthopaedics and Trauma	32	32	63	136	156	146	59
Ophthalmology	34	15	12	45	149	315	366
Dental and Oral Surgery	13	45	64	17	14	15	10
Gynaecology	2	4	359	256	106	68	24
Maternity/SCBU	255	0	15,468	0	0	0	0
Radiotheraphy	0	0	6	32	35	23	15

	Average Length of Episode 1991/2						
	0–4	5–14	15–44	45–64	65–74	75–84	85+
Male Non-elective							
Medicine and Paediatrics	3.8	3.5	6.0	9.4	9.4	11.2	11.9
Elderly Continuing Care	.0	.0	.0	.0	79.0	75.6	86.0
Surgical Specialties	4.5	3.1	4.9	9.6	12.6	13.9	12.7
ENT Surgery	1.3	1.4	4.8	7.5	16.1	7.2	4.7
Orthopaedics and Trauma	6.0	4.4	6.9	11.9	18.0	24.4	24.2
Ophthalmology	3.3	3.9	3.5	4.3	5.7	6.8	9.9
Dental and Oral Surgery	2.0	1.1	2.4	7.5	10.4	10.1	2.0
Radiotherapy	36.5	.0	6.1	11.2	12.2	10.2	31.0
Mental Illness	32.9	46.8	36.7	59.5	67.1	63.3	68.8
Female Non-elective							
Medicine and Paediatrics	3.7	3.5	5.5	9.7	9.7	11.8	12.7
Elderly Continuing Care	.0	.0	.0	.0	85.1	80.7	83.5
Surgical Specialties	4.2	2.8	5.4	10.2	14.3	15.4	14.4
ENT Surgery	2.2	1.5	2.5	5.5	6.4	8.2	7.6
Orthopaedics and Trauma	4.0	3.9	8.3	12.7	17.6	24.4	25.8
Ophthalmology	3.3	3.5	3.3	4.8	7.4	6.6	9.4
Dental and Oral Surgery	17.2	2.1	4.7	3.5	7.6	11.0	2.2
Gynaecology	.9	9.5	2.3	6.1	12.1	14.1	21.5
Radiotherapy	.0	.0	7.3	6.3	11.4	11.0	24.8
Mental Illness	105.3	68.5	40.3	56.1	65.7	61.2	61.6
Male Elective							
Medicine and Paediatrics	3.1	2.7	1.5	2.1	2.6	4.6	6.3
Elderly Continuing Care	.0	.0	.0	.0	61.7	81.6	116.3
Surgical Specialties	1.8	1.3	1.4	3.1	4.1	4.4	5.5
ENT Surgery	.8	1.1	2.0	2.7	3.5	3.3	4.3
Orthopaedics and Trauma	2.9	3.6	2.1	3.4	6.8	11.7	11.0
Ophthalmology	1.0	2.7	3.1	1.5	1.7	1.9	3.0
Dental and Oral Surgery	1.0	.3	1.3	4.3	2.4	3.1	1.4
Maternity/SCBU	15.4	.0	.0	.0	.0	.0	.0
Radiotherapy	18.4	.0	5.0	9.9	12.9	15.7	17.8
Female Elective							
Medicine and Paediatrics	3.6	1.9	1.7	2.7	2.9	4.4	6.9
Elderly Continuing Care	.0	.0	.0	.0	76.3	94.2	114.5
Surgical Specialties	2.8	1.8	1.6	2.8	4.0	4.7	4.3
ENT Surgery	.7	1.3	2.2	2.6	2.5	3.1	3.9
Orthopaedics and Trauma	3.0	4.0	2.4	4.2	8.0	10.5	14.3
Ophthalmology	1.1	1.1	.9	1.6	1.7	2.2	2.3
Dental and Oral Surgery	.9	.5	1.1	1.8	4.5	4.6	3.2
Gynaecology	1.3	.8	1.7	3.1	5.3	6.8	8.0
Maternity/SCBU	15.2	.0	3.0	.0	.0	.0	.0
Radiotherapy	4.0	.0	5.0	6.5	9.7	17.4	17.7

Research and Policy: Which Comes First?

ANDREW J RICHARDSON, Consultant in Public Health Medicine, Worcester and District Public Health Medicine Department

SUMMARY

The rhetoric of the NHS reforms suggests that health needs assessment is a starting point. The nature of health needs assessment is examined: in addition to its technical component it inevitably requires the exercise of value judgements. It is therefore a process of decision making, rather than measurement. It will be argued that building an explicit framework of values should precede the technical component of health needs assessment.

The relationship between health needs assessment and resource allocation policy is discussed in this light; implications for the development of resource allocation policy are considered.

From research to policy or from policy to research?

The title of today's conference, 'Resource allocation and health needs: from research to policy', carries the implication that research is the basis of policy. The art of policy making is often dominated by the science of research and, as a result, is seen to be secondary to it. Clearly the two activities iterate to an extent. It may be convenient, however, to view them as two complementary stages. This paper examines health needs assessment, and concludes that policy should provide the framework for research, and logically should precede it.

The nature of health and need

Health and need are not objectively defined or fixed (Bradshaw, 1972); rather they are subjective and essentially contestable concepts. They vary from person to person and in time, place, and circumstance. While the observation that health and need are subjective may appear facile it has profound implications for the assessment of local health needs.

Differences in the subjective perception of needs can result in individuals with the same level of quantifiable disease reporting widely different states of

63

health and need. For example, two people may each have osteoarthritic hips which has a comparable radiological appearance and range of mobility: this may be seen as an inconvenience by a woman who has an inactive lifestyle and lives with her daughter who looks after her, whereas another woman who is still in employment and wishes to lead an active life it presents a pressing need for a hip replacement. At a population level it is also likely that perceptions of need vary, between localities and population segments for example. To assess the need for hip replacements requires more than an objective assessment of the prevalence of radiological disease in a population (Williams et al, 1992).

The assessment of local health needs is dependent on value judgements, it does not rest solely on objective and scientific processes. Health needs assessment is a process of decision making, and not simply one of measurement. We need to agree what we mean by health needs before we can set about measuring them.

Dimensions of health needs assessment

The literature on health needs assessment focuses on its objective and scientific elements; examining data on service activity and examining the effectiveness and efficiency of interventions which improve health. The need for a 'corporate' approach has been acknowledged (NHSME, 1991), but it is often unclear how this is supposed to relate to the products of epidemiology, health economics and health technology assessment.

This paper proposes that, in addition to its scientific and technical dimension, the assessment of local health needs has an important value driven or ethical dimension. These two dimensions, the 'technical' and the 'political', might be called the art and the science of assessing health needs.

The technical dimension is underpinned by epidemiology and health economics. It is an activity which is dependent on knowledge and expertise, and is therefore largely a professional function. Despite limitations on the data available for technical needs assessment a great deal of work has already been done (for example through the Health Needs Assessment Network).

The political dimension is concerned with value judgements: valuing outcomes; setting priorities; and articulating objectives. It is a corporate or societal process, rather than one that professionals can have a claim to lead. The political dimension of health needs assessment is undoubtedly done poorly.

Which comes first?

The question of which dimension comes first is of immense practical importance as its answer carries implications for the process of assessing needs. Is it logical to define policy and then make technical judgements within its framework, or can epidemiological research lead to policy?

The need for in-vitro fertilisation (IVF) (Redmayne and Klein, 1993) offers an illustration. Questions like 'should IVF be available at all on the NHS', and 'should services ensure: equality of access, equality of outcome, or maximisation of health gain', are of a political nature. They are driven by values. More technical questions relate to estimating the number of cycles that a district should purchase, or examining the effectiveness of different modes of treatment. It is clear that to deal with the latter type of question one must first answer, or assume, the former.

It is concluded that technical judgements should follow a policy framework, rather than lead to one. This is because of the subjective nature of health and need, which means that judgements of an apparently technical and objective nature are inevitably dependent on value judgements. These value judgements, which comprise the political dimension, may be explicit but are more often hidden. Often they simply reflect the assumptions of a particular discipline (for example the health economist's view that maximising benefit is the desired outcome of health services (Donaldson and Mooney, 1991)) rather than a wider public or professional consensus. This will ultimately lead to conflict with groups who hold different assumptions. An important role for public consultation (NHSME, 1992) is to inform the framework of values which underpin the assessment of local needs.

Implications for resource allocation

The view of health needs assessment set out above suggests two lessons for resource allocation. Firstly, that the political dimension must be acknowledged in addition to the technical aspects; and secondly, that political questions should be explicitly settled, rather than be assumed.

It is perhaps easier to apply expertise to the data that is available than it is to find agreement on issues that are contestable. A consequence of this is that policy can become subsidiary to research. While there are statistical and epidemiological systems and techniques to arrive at technical judgements there is a need to develop a technology of policy-making. Our ability to resolve 'political' issues needs to be improved. Too often policy is ad hoc and a response to outside pressures. Health Authorities do not have the structure of elected and executive officers that is well established in government. Exploring ways in which the public can influence policy is a priority.

It is logical to resolve explicitly value judgements before technical ones are addressed. The alternative, where policy is driven by research, carries an inevitable danger. This is that the values implicit in the research will later be contested. This weakness undermines the whole process and is a fundamental barrier to the development of a stable and robust system for resource allocation.

References

Bradshaw (1972). A taxonomy of social need. In 'Problems and progress in medical care; essays on current research'. 7th series. McLachlan G, Editor. Oxford University Press.

Donaldson C and Mooney G (1991). Needs assessment, priority setting, and contracts for health care: an economic view. British Medical Journal, 303, 1529–1530.

NHSME (1991). Assessing health care needs. A DHA project discussion paper. NHSME.

NHSME (1992). Local voices. The views of local people in purchasing for health. NHSME.

Redmayne S and Klein R (1993). Rationing in practice: the case of in vitro fertilisation. British Medical Journal, 306, 1521–24.

Williams M, Frankel S, Nanchahal K, Coast J and Donovan J (1992). Epidemiologically based needs assessment: Total hip replacement. NHSME.

Address for contact

Dr Andrew Richardson, Department of Public Health Medicine, Worcester and District Health Authority, Isaac Maddox House, Shrub Hill, Worcester, WR4 9RW.

Resource Allocation and Health Needs – A Perspective from an Inner City District

STEPHEN J MUNDAY, Consultant in Public Health Medicine and
PAUL SHOBROOK, Health Geographer, West Birmingham Health
Authority

SUMMARY

The impact of the implementation of weighted capitation funding on an inner city district is assessed.

The population of West Birmingham Health District is relatively young, experiences high mortality rates, and has the fourth highest Jarman score in England.

The West Midland Regional Health Authority resource allocation formula includes the national set of age weights, and the SMR (under 75 years of age).

The net effect of these weights for the West Birmingham Health Authority is to increase its allocation target by 11%. However, despite this the DHA remains 14% above its weighted capitation target.

Explanations for the DHA's over-target position are explored. Analyses show that the 'excess spending' is mostly within a particular group of services: general medicine, geriatrics, primary care, mental health and learning disabilities. The 'excess spending' is mostly due to higher than average usage of services by the population and is less due to higher provider costs.

The implications of these findings for resource allocation policy, and for the West Birmingham health strategy are discussed.

Introduction

West Birmingham Health District has many of the characteristics of other inner city districts, including the problem that its present level of funding is considerably in excess of its weighted capitation 'fair-shares' target. In this paper the health and socio-economic characteristics of the district are described, the position regarding the Health Authority's current funding level and its weighted capitation target allocation is outlined, some of the analyses which have been undertaken in order to understand this position are

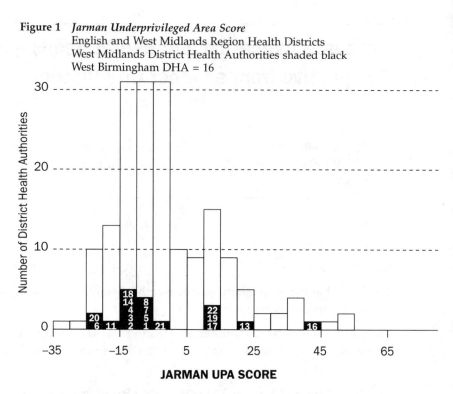

Figure 1 *Jarman Underprivileged Area Score*
English and West Midlands Region Health Districts
West Midlands District Health Authorities shaded black
West Birmingham DHA = 16

JARMAN UPA SCORE

Source: Professor Jarman (calculated from OPCS 1981 census)

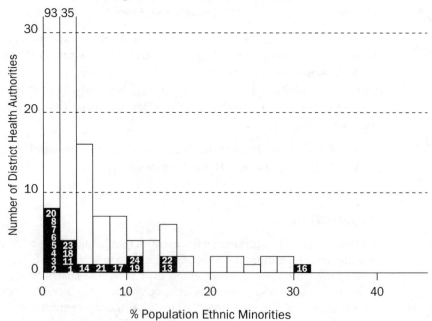

Figure 2 *Ethnic Minorities – % Population*
English and West Midlands Region Health Districts
West Midlands District Health Authorities shaded black
West Birmingham DHA = 16

% Population Ethnic Minorities

Source: OPCS 1981 Small Area Statistics

68

Figure 3 *All Cause SMRs (all ages) 1991*
English and West Midlands Health Districts
West Midlands District Health Authorities shaded black
West Birmingham DHA = 16

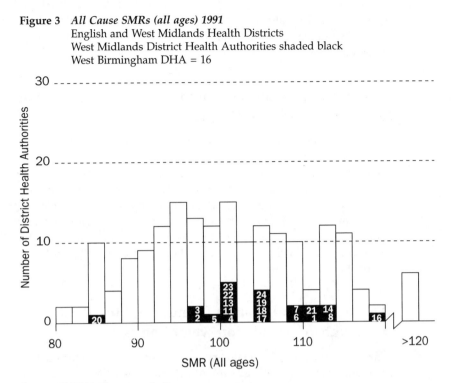

Source: DoH Performance Indicators

Figure 4 *All Cause SMR (15–64 years) 1987–91*
English and West Midlands Health Districts
West Midlands District Health Authorities shaded black
West Birmingham DHA = 16

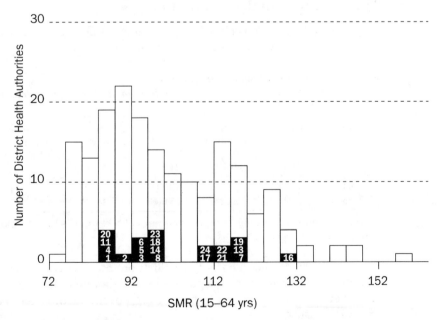

Source: DoH Performance Indicators

69

presented, and finally some of the difficulties which are likely to be experienced in reducing spending levels down towards the target allocation are assessed.

The health and socio-economic characteristics of West Birmingham Health District

The people of West Birmingham Health District are amongst the most deprived and unhealthy in the country. West Birmingham has the fourth highest Jarman score (Figure 1) and the highest proportion of people from ethnic minorities in England (Figure 2). The District has the highest mortality rate in the West Midlands Region, and one of the highest in the country (Figure 3). The mortality rate in the 15–64 years age group is considerably greater than the national and regional average (Figure 4), which lends support to the hypothesis that illness occurs at an earlier age in deprived populations than in affluent ones.

The WMRHA allocation formula and the West Birmingham population weighting factor

The West Midlands Regional Health Authority allocation formula includes as weighting factors the full, all causes SMR (for ages 0–74 years) and the national set of age weights. These weights are applied to each DHA's crude population numbers, in order to adjust for different levels of health care need. The net effect of these weights for West Birmingham is to 'increase' its population size, and therefore its target cash allocation, by a factor of 11%.

The West Birmingham allocation

The weighted capitation 'fair-shares' allocation target compared with the baseline allocation for 1993/4 is shown in Figure 5.

Figure 5 *West Birmingham Health Authority*
Weighted capitation targets and allocation figures for the periods 1993–94 and 1992–93

Period	Baseline allocation £000s	Weighted capitation share £000s	Excess spend £000s	Over target %	Increase in population due to weighting factor %
1993–94	81,164	70,723	10,441	15	11
1992–93	77,245	62,245	15,000	24	11

Source: Allocation of revenue and capital resources 1992/3 and 1993/4, WMRHA, Jan 1992 and Dec 1992.

The actual 1993/4 allocation is £10 million or 15% in excess of the target allocation derived from the weighted capitation formula. Interestingly, the same figure for 1992/3 was £15 million (24% over-target), largely because pre-1991 Census population figures were used in the calculation. This illustrates the potential volatility of the allocation formula.

Understanding the West Birmingham over-target position

It is obviously important to understand why there is such an excess level of spending over and above the fair-shares allocation target. The first task which was undertaken was to understand how the mortality and age weights determine the population weighting factor. The figure of 11% is not as high as might be expected – the weighting factor derived from the SMR alone is in the order of 20%. However, the allocation is particularly sensitive to the weighting given for age and West Birmingham has a relatively young population (Figure 6). The effect of both factors combined is to reduce the weighting factor from 20% to 11%.

Figure 6 *Population Age Profile – 1992*
England, West Midlands, West Birmingham

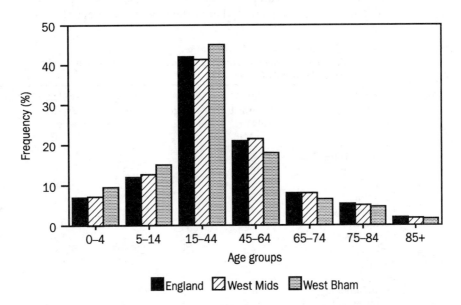

Source: Public Health Common Data Set, 1993

The age weights are derived from an analysis of national hospital utilisation rates by specific age groups. However, it is believed that in deprived populations such as West Birmingham, the age weights under-estimate the level of need in the 45–64 year age group, and over-estimate the level of need in the elderly. For example it has been shown that mortality in West Birmingham is particularly high in the 15–64 year age group (Figure 4) compared with the West Midlands or England. A preliminary analysis of spend pattern by age groups for acute inpatient services in West Birmingham suggests that spending levels are high in the 45–64 years age group, compared with the national age weights.

It has been demonstrated that there is an inverse relationship between the proportion of elderly in a population and the level of deprivation (Williams et

71

al, 1992) – the hypothesis being that there is selective migration of healthy elderly people out of deprived areas, into more affluent areas. This gives rise to a major anomaly. A formula which allocates resources preferentially to populations which have a high proportion of elderly people, will tend to discriminate against deprived populations. Further research is required into this critical issue.

The second task was to understand the OPCS population projections – a slight fall in population size was also believed to be contributing to the over-target position. It was found that the population projections for West Birmingham which had been used were unreliable and that there is considerable uncertainty regarding future population size. This point is demonstrated by the considerable change in the weighted capitation target between 1992/3 and 1993/4.

The third task was to compare the West Birmingham spend pattern for each of the main service groups with that of the Regional average (Figure 7). Excess

Figure 7 *West Birmingham Health Authority*
Analysis of spend pattern by service group 1993/4 compared with
West Midlands Region

Service Group	WBHA Contract Value (1) (£M)	WBHA Average SPH (2) (£)	WMRHA Average SPH (3) (£)	WBHA 'Excess' spend (4) (£M)	Variance (5) %
Learning Difficulties	6.9	33	20	2.6	63%
Mental Health	10.9	51	39	2.6	32%
Geriatrics	7.0	250	192	1.6	30%
Maternity	5.6	118	110	0.4	8%
Gynaecology	2.2	26	20	0.5	32%
Paediatrics	2.3	45	49	−0.2	−9%
General Medical	13.1	62	44	3.7	40%
General Surgical	8.1	38	30	1.8	27%
T & O	5.2	25	19	1.1	27%
ENT	1.7	8	5	0.6	62%
Ophthalmology	1.2	6	5	0.2	29%
Community/primary	10.2	48	37	2.5	30%
Other	10.2	47	26	4.8	81%
Total (6)	84.6	398	298	22.3	34%

Notes:
1 Contract value = total spend in each service group
2 Average SPH = Spend Per Head of population in each service group
3 West Midlands Region average Spend Per Head of population.
4 'Excess spend' = WBHA contract value (col 1)
   – contract value if WMRHA average SPH applied (col 3 × WB population)
.5 Variance = (WBHA SPH (col 2) – WMRHA SPH (Col 3))/WMRHA SPH × 100%
6 The total WBHA spend of 84.6 million is comprised of the £81.2 million base
   allocation (see Figure 5) plus other additions

spending over and above the Regional average occurs in mental health, learning difficulties, geriatrics, general medicine and primary/community care. An examination of the access rates, and costs where they are available, illustrates that the excess spend pattern is mostly due to a higher usage of service by the population rather than to high local provider prices.

Achieving the weighted capitation target

The development of a strategy to reduce spending levels and to achieve the weighted capitation target is obviously problematic. Firstly, a view needs to be taken about what is the appropriate level of spending in each service. It can not be assumed that the Regional spend pattern is appropriate for the West Birmingham population, but it does at least serve as a useful guide for comparison. Services where spending levels are in excess of the West Midlands average have therefore been reviewed.

Spending levels on services for people with learning disabilities are dependent on the number of residents in long stay hospitals – West Birmingham has the highest prevalence in the West Midlands Region. This is despite an extensive resettlement programme in recent years. This situation has resulted from historic service provision levels – in both health and social services, and historic health and social policy. This point is illustrated by the fact that some people were first admitted to long stay hospitals as early as 1920 – most were admitted in the 1960s or before (Figure 8). In addition the age profile of these patients (Figure 9) shows that although there is a wide range from 20 to 80 years, three quarters of hospital residents are aged less than 60 years. A reduction in the numbers by 'natural' processes is likely to be slow. The costs of caring for these people are not avoidable in the short term and bridging finance is required in order to facilitate hospital closure and resettlement.

Mental health services issues are similar to those of learning disabilities. It is not believed that there is scope for significant reductions in spending.

Figure 8 *People With Learning Difficulties*
Year of Admission

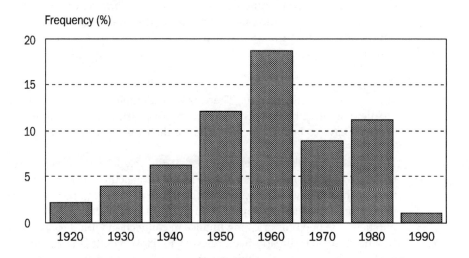

West Birmingham residents in long stay hospitals 1992

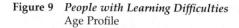

Figure 9 *People with Learning Difficulties*
Age Profile

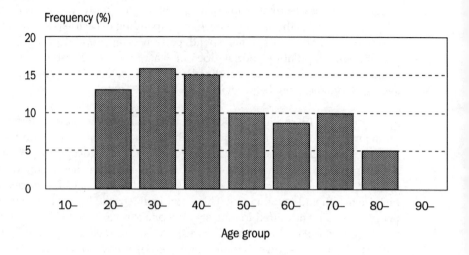

West Birmingham residents in long stay hospitals 1992

The development of primary/community care is both national and local policy. Maintaining spending at current levels is desirable if only because of the implications of the Community Care Act, and the likely changes in secondary care provision (for example, shorter lengths of hospital stay). There is certainly little scope for reducing spending in these services.

General medicine and geriatrics are perhaps the most likely candidates for spending reductions, although it should be remembered that much of the burden of ill-health is shouldered by these services, and much of the workload is of an emergency nature. Considerable improvements in health status, and improvements in primary care are therefore required, before significant reductions in spending will be achieved.

Finally, an analysis of GP spend patterns illustrates a further difficulty of implementation (Figure 10). There is considerable variation in the use of inpatient services by each GP practice in West Birmingham – 'high' referring GPs will have to be influenced to reduce their use of secondary care.

The conclusion which is reached is that the major part of the current £10 million 'excess spend' will need to be found from acute services, and probably from within elective surgery. In fact the figure will need to be in excess of £10 million if policies to develop community care and health promotion are also pursued. The need for bridging finance in connection with the closure of long stay hospitals has already been referred to. However, this is equally true for other services – change of this magnitude is very costly.

Figure 10 *West Birmingham GP Practices*
Spend Per Head – Acute Inpatient Services Only, 1992/93

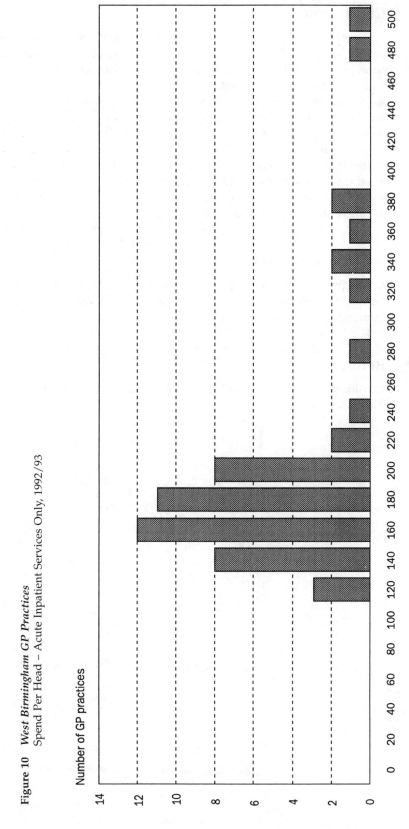

Conclusion

In conclusion, there are a number of key issues. Firstly, the assessment of health care needs is an integral component of resource allocation. Resource allocation is therefore as much a public health issue as it is a financial one. Secondly, the current WMRHA resource allocation formula does not adequately reflect the health care needs of West Birmingham residents. Indeed, this is probably also true of other inner city districts, in other Regions. In particular, the age weights used in the formula discriminate against socio-economically deprived districts. Thirdly, even if it is accepted that the current WMRHA allocation policy is 'correct' and equitable then it should be recognised that achieving the weighted capitation target spending levels is fraught with difficulties – particularly if at the same time other policy objectives, such as care in the community, are being pursued.

Address for contact

Dr Stephen Munday, Department of Public Health Medicine, North Birmingham Healthcare Purchasing Consortium, 1 Vernon Rd, Edgbaston, Birmingham, B16 9SA.

Reference

1. Williams E S, Scott C, Brazil R. NHS distribution of funds unfair. BMJ 1992; 304: 643. (letter).

The Practicalities of Developing and Implementing Resource Allocation Policies

MARTIN DOVE, Deputy Regional Director of Finance, South Western
Regional Health Authority

SUMMARY

The presentation examines the current NHS resource allocation framework and identifies a range of factors which affect the development and
implementation of resource allocation policies which take account of
research findings.

The objective of NHS resource allocation policy is broadly defined as
being: 'to achieve equity of distribution of resources relative to health
needs'.

The factors affecting the development and implementation of these
policies are explored in relation to the components of the resource
allocation framework which are identified as:

>   the structure which determines at which point decisions about
>   equitable distribution are made

>   the basis used for determining equity in relation to health needs

>   the judgement exercised in moving towards an equitable distribu-
>   tion (the pace of change)

Recurring themes include:

>   the political environment

>   the constraints of national policy

>   the balancing of a responsive approach with the need for stability
>   focusing research at the right level

>   problems of communication

Introduction

Resource allocation in the NHS is mainly concerned with distributing
resources according to relative need and is not concerned with absolute need.
Resource allocation is a broad subject and decisions on distribution permeate

the NHS. It is not just about capitation formulae, but forms an integral part of priority setting. There are a number of practical difficulties in developing and implementing resource allocation policies which take account of research findings.

The objective of resource allocation in the NHS can be broadly defined as being:

'To achieve equity of distribution relative to health needs'

Linking Research and Policy

There are perhaps two interrelated factors which inhibit the links between research and policy. The first is the need for useable research findings, which can be taken and practically applied and used in the NHS. The second is the complex NHS resource allocation framework.

Useable Research

Useable research has to be convincing to the research community, but it also has to be plausible to health service managers who have to take the results of research and apply them in the development of resource allocation policies. In addition research results have to be reconcilable to subjective views of relative needs and must be capable of application to substantial issues at the appropriate level within the NHS structure. The results of research should be robust and easily maintainable over time. For example will information be available in an updated form and will it still be relevant when populations and other circumstances change? However complicated the research, the results must be presented in a simple fashion and be capable of communication to the right people at the right level. Normally the NHS user of research has to communicate the results onwards to other NHS decision makers and practitioners.

The Resource Allocation Framework

There are three components to the resource allocation framework: the complex NHS structure, the basis used to determine equity and the judgement actually exercised in implementing the move towards equitable distribution (pace of change).

The basis for distribution of resources is where research is expected to be the most useful. However, given the pre-requisite of usable research, the complex resource allocation structure and difficulties in developing suitable bases of distribution, this often results in policy taking the lead with research being undertaken to provide evidence to support the policy.

Having developed new research based policy, it is unrealistic to ignore the practical problems of implementing new resource allocation policies. Judgement is required in determining the pace of change, in assessing the political environment, and in appreciating the need to create a stable environment so that consumers of the health service can have confidence in what is being provided. Often the easiest method of implementation is through levelling up below-target users rather than withdrawing services from over-target users.

Conclusions

In conclusion there are a range of factors which affect the development and implementation of resource allocation policies which take account of research findings. These include the importance of useable research, the complex resource allocation framework in the NHS and the judgement exercised in moving towards an equitable basis of distribution.

Address for Contact

Mr Martin Dove, Finance Department, South Western Regional Health Authority, King Square House, 26/27 King Square, Bristol, BS2 8EF.

Translating Research into Practice – from Rhetoric to Reality

BOBBIE JACOBSON, Director of Public Health, East London & The City Health Authority

SUMMARY

This paper will look at the realities of translating the findings from research given the existing constraints. It will look at the barriers preventing an equitable allocation of resources by drawing on specific examples from within an inner city population in London. These will include resource allocation at District-wide level; developing an equitable framework for allocating growth funds and the development of an equitable policy in relation to one specific intervention. It will, where possible, draw on recent experience of inequities in policy and resource allocation between geographical localities now merged within one District.

Introduction

This paper will consider what we need to do to close the gap between research and its implementation. I hope to draw out some of the principles of overcoming the barriers to allocating resources in relation to health need. I will also give some examples of how, in East London, we have tried to use the findings of research, and translate them into real change.

Equitable Resource Allocation – The Hurdles

The range of 'hurdles' may be considered under the following headings:
- Political Agenda
- Local Community Interests
- Local Professional (Provider) Interests
- Purchaser 'Perplexity Syndrome'
- Insufficient Investment/Confidence in Public Health

One must not forget that the political agenda is an external one, both national and local and influenced by numerous Government Departments. The Chancellor of the Exchequer is probably the most important health educator we have at national level. There is also the local political agenda. In East London many of the issues we want to tackle relate to work we are doing with local authorities in promoting health and preventing disease, and in terms of the community care agenda. Local politicians often have very different concepts of geographical equity and resource allocation from those who work in the Health Service. Any proposed shift of resources away from one neighbourhood to another on the grounds of need, might not be welcomed locally.

We also have to pay attention to local community interests, particularly with the new climate of 'responding to local voices'. The Community Health Council should always be invoked as well as the voluntary sector and the user. Local provider interests often use powerful shroud-waving arguments. All too often their message to us is to buy history.

Another problem is what I call the 'purchaser perplexity' syndrome, which relates to understanding which aspects of the health needs assessment relate to values, and which to the technical issues and which to the political climate in which we work. Purchasers and commissioners have had their noses rubbed in the idea that every competing interest and perception of health need has to be taken into account. However we do not yet have a system by which to attribute a specific value to technical assessment of needs or to give a relative value to, for example, the views of the local Age Concern or MIND group.

It will be also difficult to make progress if commissioning agencies do not have adequate resources or confidence in their public health function. This leaves items open to decision-making based on competing prejudices.

Shifting Resources Equitably – Overcoming the Reticence

It is important to consider the factors which are important in overcoming the reticence to make changes towards allocating resources more equitably. One issue is the need to clarify the values of the DHA and FHSA. In East London & The City we have decided to spend time involving both our non-executive and executive directors in this issue, looking at questions such as what do we mean by rationing and whose views do we take into account, etc.

I have been convinced relatively recently of the need for Health Authorities to tap their internal resources in an integrated and efficient way. This means that Directors of Finance, Public Health, Purchasing/Planning and Quality should not spend time arguing about who owns the health strategy: hopefully we all own it and must draw from one another's resources jointly. For the Director of Public Health it means using her/his independent and corporate status wisely.

It is also important that researchers ask the right questions. Sometimes researchers, whilst well meaning, get side-tracked. They ask difficult questions or ones that take three to five years to resolve, when health authorities want the answer by yesterday. This is a significant problem which somehow has to be overcome. The example I would cite concerns the post-Tomlinson changes in the configuration of health services in London, which produced several consultation documents. It seemed to us that many of the statements in the consultation document on the proposed closure of St Bartholomew's Accident and Emergency Department were unsubstantiated and worth challenging. So nearly everyone in the public health department dropped what they were doing and became involved in a month-long prospective study of A & E. The findings of our study were published the day before the closure of the consultation document and showed, in our view, the consultation document had not got it right. This opened up the whole debate about what alternative services need to be put in place if the Accident & Emergency department at St Bartholomew's closed. Our Region subsequently commissioned an independent assessment of need which took a less biased sample than our prospective study, but came to the same conclusions. The timeliness of trying to do research that is do-able and that answers questions that relate to local change is critically important. It is a difficult debate between public health practitioners who are involved at the implementation end and academic colleagues who may wish to be involved but also have international and national agendas to fulfil. Clearly translating research into policy seems like an easy thing to say, but I am aware that some of the best research which has been done by colleagues of mine is still sitting on a shelf. I wonder why, when we have assessed unmet health and social need in elderly people we have not yet found a mechanism of translating that into the contractual process, or into joint commissioning. I have created a policy unit in my Public Health directorate to help co-ordinate this process and to translate into practice some of the things that researchers genuinely find difficult.

The principle issues in overcoming barriers may be summarised as:
- Clarifying DHA/FHSA values
- Integrated working: internally and intersectorally
- Sufficient internal resources to tackle questions
- Asking the 'right' questions
- Involving the 'right' people at the outset, internally and externally
- Timely questions
- Translating research into policy/strategy for achievable change
- Making research findings widely known
- Generating the support of interested parties.

Allocation of Growth Monies

An example from the outgoing City & Hackney Health Authority illustrates an approach to allocating resources equitably, although it is flawed and open to criticism. Unlike many inner city authorities, City & Hackney Health Authority was actually a capitation gainer with just under one million pounds of growth monies in 1992. Although only a drop in the ocean in a budget of about £100 million, I was determined we should attempt to create an explicit priority-setting framework to allocate this additional money.

In the initial stage of the process the Growth Monies were divided into four categories. Over half, £540,000, went to the 'pre-emptions' or 'untouchables', like medium secure services or pressures on the acute contract. Of the rest, £115,000 was allocated to health promotion and disease prevention, and £226,000 to health care, whilst £55,000 was targeted to helping the purchasing organisation become more effective.

A two-tier system was developed to set priorities for what projects were finally to be recommended for funding. Firstly, an overall list of priority areas was generated. Bids were then called for, and each proposal was weighted in

Figure 1 *Method of Weighting Priorities for DHA*

A Priority Cited By:	Possible Score
National Health Service Management Executive (NHSME)	0–1
Health of the Nation	0–1
Regional Health Authority	0–1
District Health Authority Purchasing Plan	0–1
Objective Evidence of Local Need (Annual Reports/Local Research)	0–5
Black & Ethnic Minority Need	0–1
Total Possible Score	10

relation to a number of set criteria. The ranked proposals were then allocated resources according to what was available.

Figure 1 shows the first level of prioritisation, designed to focus on allocating resources in relation to need as identified by the various influencing factors – NHSME, the Government's Health of the Nation strategy, RHA, DHA, local factors. It was intended to show accountability and to create a middle way in the dichotomy between proper assessment of need and the political and ethical climates.

Drawing on all the strategy and guidance documents received from the Region and the NHSME about priority areas of work, we then drew up a list of priority areas. The weighting scheme shown in Figure 1 was used to score each topic, resulting in the ranking shown in Figure 2. For example, as heart disease and stroke was identified as a priority by all constituencies it received the maximum score of 10. Although alcohol and drugs was regarded as a priority on the basis of evidence of local need, it did not score as highly overall.

Figure 2 *Priorities for DHA Expenditure 1992/93*

Rank	Topic/Area	Score
1	Heart Disease/Stroke (also Nutrition, Smoking, Exercise, Blood Pressure)	10
2	Pregnancy/Infant Health	9
3	Service Quality (including Asthma)	8
4	Fertility/Women's Health (including Cancer Screening)	8
5	Child Health (including Accidents and Immunisation)	8
6	Integration with Primary Care	8
7	Mental Health	7
8	Waiting Lists	7
9	Black & Ethnic Minority Services	7
10	Diabetes	6
11	HIV/AIDS	6
12	Communicable Disease	5–6
13	Community Care (including Community Health Services)	6
14	Alcohol/Drugs	4–5
15	Food/Waterborne Disease	4
16	Environmental Quality	2
17	Day Surgery	2
18	Rehabilitation	1
Total Possible Score		10

The first stage of this approach to assessment of health need and resource allocation tended to be skewed by national and regional imperatives. To balance this the DHA felt it was legitimate to deliberately give extra weighting in the scoring scheme for local perspectives of need, and for black and ethnic minority issues which did not necessarily feature in a national perspective.

In the second stage local interest groups were invited to submit bids for funding for specific projects, and about 200 proposals were received. As it happened, being a London inner city district that was a RAWP loser for so long, when we discovered that we might have an extra one million pounds to spend, nobody knew what to do! There was some panic because we did not have a trousseau of proposals for implementing and developing services. As the decision on which projects to support had to be carried out between December 15th and Christmas it was difficult to consult with local communities. All the proposals were sent to the Community Health Council and to the local GP forum; and those proposals they identified as high priority were given a score of 1 by the DHA. A negative score was also given to any proposals that were likely to be funded from other sources, with projects relating to HIV/AIDS being the prime example of this.

Each proposal was assessed and scored on seven factors, detailed in Figure 3.

Figure 3 *Criteria for Weighting Individual Proposals*

	Criterion	Possible Score
1	Robustness/Implementability of Proposal	0 to +3
2	Promotion of Equity	0 to +1
3	Evidence of Effectiveness/Cost Effectiveness	0 to +2
4	Collaboration with/Integration with Primary Care	0 to +3
5	Prioritised by CHC	0 to +1
6	Prioritised by GPs/GP Forum	0 to +1
7	Other Possible/More Appropriate Sources of Funding	0 to −5
Total Possible Score		11

There is much rhetoric about only investing in cost-effective services. However there is very little evidence about the cost-effectiveness of specific projects, so to follow the rhetoric would mean disbanding and ceasing to purchase about 80% of health services! Most of the proposals submitted scored 0 under category 3 (Evidence of effectiveness/cost effectiveness) in the DHA weighting scheme, except where there was some local knowledge of effectiveness and cost-effectiveness.

The issues raised by City & Hackney's process for prioritising proposals for funding from the growth monies may be summarised as follows:
- Were we supporting real growth or existing commitments?
- How far should there be equity between priority areas?
- Arbitrary divisions were clearly made to cut the 'growth cake' between:
  Pre-emptions
  Health Promotion
  Health Care
  Efficiency

- The problems of consulting local interests in a timely way and the relative weighting to be given to their views

In particular it became apparent that we funded several good initiatives which were supported by 'tapering soft monies'; thereby not really providing a *growth* in services but maintaining services which would otherwise have been at risk.

I maintain that the approach adopted by the City & Hackney for the allocation of Growth Monies, if not creative accounting, is a sort of creative epidemiology. We tried not to create a dichotomy between the technical research findings and the political climate, but to bring them closer together.

Resource Allocation and Research

Turning to the question about whether it is policy that comes first or research. We would be epidemiological imperialists if we thought that epidemiology would determine resource allocation in isolation from other factors. I have tried to think of one major national health initiative over the last decade that has genuinely been determined by research findings. I thought the breast screening programme and the Forrest report came close, but then I remembered the investment was made in the run up to a general election. I wondered if the investment would have been made if there had not been the forthcoming election, or whether there would have been a repeat of what happened when cervical screening was first introduced, where the Government and the Department of Health said it was a priority, but no new resources were allocated to it so we had to borrow from Peter to pay Paul.

Address for contact

Dr Bobbie Jacobson, Public Health Directorate, East London and The City Health Authority, 97–99 Bow Rd, London, E3 2AN.

Resource Allocation in the West Midlands: analysis at the ED level and the urban/rural divide

CINDY BILLINGHAM, ANDREA THOMAS; WMRHA Information
Department
ESTELLE GILMAN, LILLIAN SOMERVAILLE & ROD GRIFFITHS;
Institute of Public & Environmental Health, The University of
Birmingham

SUMMARY

Further to the analysis that has been done, at the ward level, to investigate the possible inclusion of the Townsend deprivation index into the West Midlands RHA resource allocation formula, work has now begun at the level of the enumeration district (ED).

This paper will look at the provisional findings of this study with particular reference to the West Midlands population divided in terms of a rural and urban classification.

The method of allocating Townsend scores at the ED level would provide a mechanism by which the funding of GP fundholders secondary care budgets could be set in the same framework as the District Health Authority allocation.

Introduction

Much of the work on resource allocation carried out since RAWP (DHSS 1976) has been based on the statistical analysis of data at the small area level such as the electoral ward, or in cases where the electoral ward populations are small, combinations of wards (DHSS 1988, Carstairs 1989, Townsend 1989). However, the more diverse the population of the ward, the greater the problems incurred in this type of ecological analysis. Such problems are reduced as the areas and populations concerned are reduced in size.

In the 1991 census the data has been collated in such a way as to facilitate analysis at the very fine level of the enumeration district (ED), and it is this level of area analysis that we report on here. Data from the census, at ED level, has been used to study the effects of material deprivation on the need for health care provision.

Following from earlier ward based analysis of West Midlands data (IPEH 1992), populations, this time at the ED level, have been classified according to their Townsend score to represent the level of material deprivation experienced in that area. The EDs are then sorted by their scores and grouped into larger, non-contiguous populations of similar deprivation levels. The greater resolution possible at the ED level enabled 29 Townsend groups of EDs to be assembled. Hospital in-patient episode data has again been used in an analysis of the relationship between material deprivation and the need for health care services.

1991 Census data at the ED level

1991 census data for the region was supplied to the WMRHA by the OPCS for 11,139 EDs. However several EDs were deleted from the database before the analysis was begun. These were deleted if:

- the ED had zero resident population
- the ED was restricted to preserve confidentiality
- at least one Townsend denominator was less than 20

This left a total of 10,774 EDs.

Calculation of the Townsend score

In order to calculate the Townsend index, the following variables were extracted from the 1991 census data for each ED:

- % economically active residents who are unemployed
- % households which do not possess a car
- % households which are not owner occupied
- % households with more than one person per room

For each census variable a transformation was made to improve the normality of the distribution of that variable. The variables were then standardised by using their regional means and standard normal deviates, and the Townsend score arrived at for each ED by summing the standardised variables.

Since the scores have been standardised by regional data, they show the deprivation status of each ED *relative to all the other EDs in the region*. The scores range from −8.5 (relatively affluent) to +8.8 (relatively deprived). EDs were then sorted and divided into groups according to the nearest half Townsend score. At the extremes of the distribution any ED with a Townsend score of less than −6.25 was classed as −6.5 and any ED with a Townsend score of greater than or equal to +7.25 was classed as +7.5. This led to 29 Townsend groups.

Classification of Urban and Rural Areas

In order to classify the region into rural and urban populations, an OPCS classification of urbanisation was used (Craig 1985). This states that:

- if population density <25 people per hectare the area is defined as *rural* (according to OPCS this could include rural industrial and suburban areas)

- if population density >= 25 people per hectare the area is defined as *urban*

At present population densities are available at the ward level only from the 1991 census data, so to classify EDs into *urban* or *rural* areas, all the EDs falling within a ward were assigned to that ward's classification.

The distribution of Townsend scores across the region is shown graphically in Figure 1.

Figure 1 *Distribution of grouped Townsend scores for rural and urban EDs in the West Midlands Regional Health Authority (1991 census)*

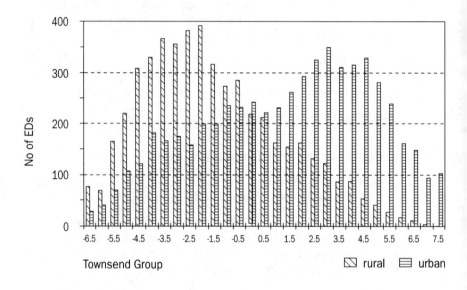

It is clear that the *urban* population and the *rural* population make up two distinct distributions with respect to the Townsend score. *Rural* populations tend to be classed towards the lower, more affluent scores, while the *urban* populations tend to be distributed towards the higher, more deprived scores. However, there is considerable overlap and both populations span almost the whole range of Townsend groups.

Deprivation and the need for health care provision

Hospital in-patient episode data from the 1991/1992 Regional Information System, containing finished consultant episodes for all specialties and all ages, was used as a proxy for health care need. Each hospital in-patient record was matched by its postcode to an ED. Five postcodes were found to be heavily duplicated, accounting for 395 records, and were removed. Of the remaining episodes only 1.8% could not be successfully matched, which left 969,887 records. Episodes for each Townsend group population were then indirectly standardised relative to the regional population by sex and 10 year age bands to produce standardised episode ratios (SERs).

A simple linear population weighted regression analysis was then carried out for the population as a whole, and for the population of the West Midlands divided into *rural* and *urban* communities.

The results from the regression analysis for the *rural* population are shown in Figure 2 and in Figure 3 for the *urban* population.

Figure 2   *Standardised episode ratios (SERs) 1991/92 data for Townsend population groups in the West Midlands Regional Health Authority: Rural areas*
SER = 95.6 + 4.6 (Townsend)

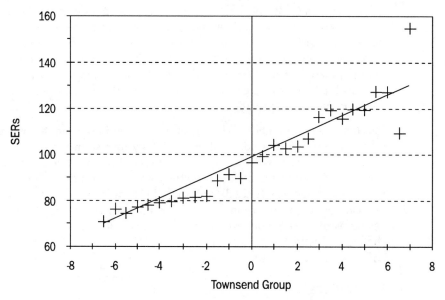

Figure 3   *Standardised episode ratios (SERs) 1991/92 data for Townsend population groups in the West Midlands Regional Health Authority: Urban areas*
SER = 99.4 + 4.5 (Townsend)

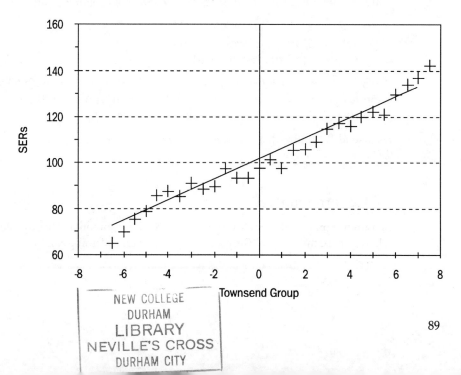

A *t* statistic was calculated to test if the regression slopes for the *rural* populations differed from that for the *urban* population. A *t* value of 0.61 was obtained, which shows that the two slopes are not statistically significantly different from each other (p>0.25).

Conclusions

The use of ED level data is a major step forward from the previous ward based analysis in that it markedly reduces the problems arising from the ecological fallacy. The relevance of the Townsend score as an index of material deprivation in both rural and urban populations has sometimes been questioned, particularly with reference to the use of the NO CAR variable. However, in this study the Townsend index appears to be behaving in a very similar way in both populations classified as *rural* and those classified as *urban*, in that the relationship between increasing need for health care provision with increasing levels of material deprivation is similar in both populations.

The analysis reported here, which groups together EDs of similar deprivation status, also provides a potential methodology for use in the secondary care allocation process to GPFHs. There is an urgent need to provide an equitable resource allocation methodology between services funded from the DHA budgets and services funded from the GPFH budgets. Since GP catchment areas are often not co-terminus with ward boundaries it would be difficult to extend ward based models to encompass GPFHs. However at the ED level this should be possible.

References

Carstairs V & Morris R (1989). *Deprivation, mortality and resource allocation* Comm Med 11 364–372

Craig J (1985). *Ward population trends 1971 to 1981.* OPCS Population Trends No 42

DHSS (1976). *Sharing resources for health in England: report of the Resource Allocation Working Party* London HMSO

DHSS (1988). *Review of the Resource Allocation Working Party formula* NHSME Institute of Public & Environmental Health (Internal report) (1992) *Deprivation & the West Midlands RHA resource allocation formula*

Townsend P, Phillimore P, Beattie A (1989). *Health and deprivation; inequality in the North.* Routledge

Address for contact

Dr Lillian Somervaille, Institute of Public & Environmental Health, Medical School, The University of Birmingham, Edgbaston, Birmingham, B15 2TT.

From Needs to Services: a Case Study of Older People with Visual Problems

URSULA HARRIES, RACHEL LANDES, Public Health Research and
Resource Centre (Bolton, Salford, Trafford and Wigan DHAs)
MARIOTH MANCHÉ, Consultant in Public Health, Bolton DHA
CHRISSIE PICKIN, Health Gain Consultant, Salford DHA

SUMMARY

Research around health needs assessment will be key to a reformed
NHS in which resource allocation is to be shaped by rational research
based decision-making. The challenge of this is using information
related to 'need' to change the pattern of services. This paper considers
the difficulties inherent in this process and factors which may improve
the interface between research and policy.

In 1991, the PHRRC undertook research to collect information on the
health and social care needs of older people with visual problems.
Following this, centre staff have been working with health authority
staff to identify the implications of research findings for purchasing.
Information was collected through reviewing the literature, interviews
with older people who had vision problems (and a linked clinical
assessment of a sub-sample of those interviewed) and through reviewing current service provision. The study took place in four district health
authorities. Issues raised included: equity of service provision to different client groups, access to services, and the effectiveness and appropriateness of services.

The paper focuses on activities in two of the four districts to illustrate
ways in which 'health needs assessment' might shape service provision.
It will explore the following themes:

> the difference between needs identification and needs assessment
> and the important role for researchers and policy makers in each
>
> how decisions are made on resource allocation on the basis of
> research and what flexibility there is for change in the short term
>
> barriers to change including:
>> organisational and professional inertia
>> vested interests
>> budgetary inflexibility

the nature and speed of organisational change in the NHS

the limits of contract driven change and the division of responsibility for service development between service providers and NHS purchasers

the status of lay perspectives in the process

The paper draws out the difficulties that will need to be overcome if the health needs assessment process is to inform the purchasing of health and social care.

Introduction

In the golden future of the reformed NHS resource allocation is to be shaped by rational research based decision-making. A key part of this research will be around health needs assessment. However, the challenge of this is not so much in identifying needs, but in using information related to 'need' to change the pattern of services. This paper considers the difficulties inherent in this process and factors which may improve the interface between research and policy, using one research project as a 'case study'.

In 1991, the PHRRC undertook research to collect information on the health and social care needs of older people with visual problems. Information was collected from several sources:

- reviewing the literature
- interviews with older people who had vision problems (and a linked clinical assessment of a sub-sample of those interviewed[1])
- a review of current health and social service provision, including interviews with key provider managers in social services
- focus groups with older people in one health district[2]

The key issues raised during the 'needs identification' process can be summarised as follows:

1 Equity
There was evidence of *inequity* of service provision. The vast majority of NHS resources go to the hospital sector, yet the survey and literature review showed that the largest cause of visual disability is maculopathy, which cannot be treated medically or surgically. This means that the majority of people with visual disabilities receive little or no health service provision.

2 Accessibility
Most people with visual disabilities had seen their GP in the last 12 months, but had little or no contact with other services. Few people were registered blind or partially-sighted.

3 Effectiveness
The analysis of the hospital activity data showed that one of the 4 districts has a hospitalisation rate for ophthalmology which was almost 50% lower than the other 3 districts. There were however no significant differences in the prevalence of visual problems assessed in the local surveys in each of the 4 districts.

4   Social Acceptability

Many health professionals raised the issue of the possible stigmatising effect of registration. However, registration for blind and partial sight is one of the main routes for accessing specialist social services.

Following the information gathering, or 'needs identification' stage, centre staff have been working with health authority staff to identify possible implications of the research findings for purchasing. An interim project report was produced for discussion in each of the authorities (Harries et al, 1993). Different models of working together were adopted in each district, depending on existing structures and ways of working. The process of relating research findings to policy decisions was least problematic in the district which had an existing 'project group' set up partly in response to the research.

We have identified the following developments which have taken place partly as a result of the work carried out:

- 2 new contracts for rehabilitation services and low vision aid clinics; these contracts are recurrent and were set up using development monies in one district
- waiting list monies used for extra cataract operations
- development of local guidelines for services: aimed at improving communication between different sectors of the service. One district has funded a researcher to work as a facilitator with local groups set up to explore how inter-sectoral communication might be improved.

Concluding Comments: developing a knowledge-based service

The world of research and resource allocation differ in many ways. Both researchers and purchasers need to develop a reasonable understanding of the constraints under which their colleagues are working. The idea of a knowledge-based NHS where services are 'need-led' is in its infancy. Researchers must be aware that research is only one of many factors which influence the pattern of services. The historical pattern will be supported by vested interests even when research data suggest that a shift in the pattern of provision would make the service more sensitive to local needs.

However, research can play some part in the resource allocation process. The nature and speed of organisational change in the NHS can often put up barriers to research being taken seriously as the service becomes introspective, rather than innovative and outward-looking.

Notes

1. The clinical assessments were carried out by Richard Wormald and colleagues from the Royal Western Ophthalmic Hospital.

2. The focus groups were carried out in conjunction with Gareth Williams, University of Salford.

Acknowledgements

The research reported here was funded by the NHSME (Project 26) and the North West RHA.

References

Harries U, Leventhall R and Popay J (1993). Assessing the health and social care needs of visually disabled older people: An interim project report. PHRRC Research report 1.

Address for contact

Dr Ursula Harries, Public Health Research and Resource Centre, 4 Acton Square, Off The Crescent, Salford, M5 4NY.

Purchasing an IVF/GIFT Service for East Sussex

CYNTHIA LYONS, Department of Public Health Medicine, East Sussex
Health Authority

SUMMARY

Subfertility is a health care problem which has very definite physiological, psychological and social implications. Commissioners of health care have to make decisions about the resources to devote to subfertility services within the context of district fertility services and competing demands for scarce resources from other sectors.

An assessment of need for an IVF/GIFT service was undertaken to inform the 1993/94 Purchasing Plan. The resultant report, which integrated epidemiological information with the results of a survey of consultants in obstetrics and gynaecology in East Sussex and information on costs, success rates and patient selection from local IVF/GIFT centres, presented recommendations on the nature and level of service to be purchased and costed options for purchasing the service.

In essence, the report recommended that 62 cycles of IVF should be purchased from one of two named centres and that a maximum of two cycles of IVF should be made available to women who are less than 40 years and have nil or one child.

Further work produced a clinical policy which set out the inclusion criteria to be used to identify those couples eligible for the service.

Having determined a budget, based on an estimate of costs and minimum number of cycles needed, a service specification was drawn up and the identified units invited to tender for the contract.

Introduction

An assessment of need for an Invitro Fertilisation (IVF)/Gamete Intrafallopian Transfer (GIFT) service for East Sussex was undertaken in order to inform the 1993/94 Purchasing Plan. (IVF involves surgically collected eggs and sperm being mixed together in the laboratory to fertilise under glass and the fertilised eggs being transferred to the uterus after a couple of days via the cervical canal. GIFT is used to place sperm and surgically collected eggs in the fallopian tube for fertilisation to take place.) The resultant report, which integrated epidemiological information, the results of a survey of consultants in obstetrics and gynaecology in East Sussex, and information from local IVF/GIFT centres, presented recommendations on the nature and level of service to be purchased and costed options for purchasing the service.

Epidemiology

The main causes of subfertility are shown in Figure 1, but it is important to remember that a significant proportion of couples will have more than one cause.

Figure 1   *Causes of Subfertility (Hull et al, 1985)*

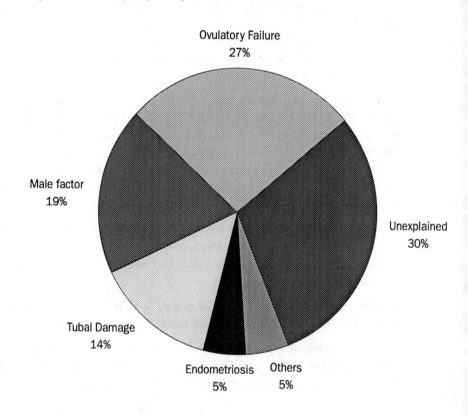

It is proposed that a lifetime incidence of subfertility in a district is 17%, that is one in six of couples will need the help of a specialist subfertility clinic at some time in their lives (Hull et al, 1985). It is argued that this describes a minimum picture and represents an annual incidence of 1.2 couples per 1000 total population (Hull et al, 1985). It has been estimated that a health authority (popn c.250,000) with an established subfertility service may expect 230 new consultant referrals each year of which 111 will need IVF/GIFT (Effective Health Care, 1992).

Effectiveness of GIFT/IVF

Only IVF can be used to bypass blocked tubes, as GIFT depends on at least one healthy fallopian tube. IVF will detect poor fertilisation but GIFT will not, which is one of the problems of using GIFT without first demonstrating that fertilisation is possible.

Aggregate data from the Human Fertilisation and Embryology Authority (HFEA) show that in 1990 the average pregnancy rate with IVF was 17% per treatment cycle, (average maternity rate of 12% per treatment cycle, 14% per couple treated because some couples had more than one cycle). The average number of treatment cycles per patient in 1991 in the UK was 1.16.

The success of IVF appears to decrease with women over 40 years old and accurately diagnosed male factor subfertility.

Survey of Consultants

A self-administered postal questionnaire sent to all ten consultant gynaecologists in East Sussex elicited an 80% response rate. The survey showed that 18–19 new subfertile patients and 50–54 follow-up patients were seen per week across East Sussex.

It was found that there were approximately 5–6 patients sent for NHS IVF/ GIFT treatment per year and between 56 and 61 private patients. The consultants thought that if there were an easily accessible free service they might send between 115 and 146 patients for IVF/GIFT, approximately double the number going privately. The survey also showed that IVF/GIFT patients were being sent to eight different centres.

It is important that treatment is given to those for whom it is likely to be effective and to those in greatest need so the questionnaire also sought recommendations for inclusion and exclusion criteria. A number of different criteria were recommended but there was some agreement on maternal age and parity.

Survey of Specialist Centres

There are twenty-four 'local' centres within an acceptable travelling distance. These centres were contacted and asked to supply information on costs, success rates and patient selection.

It was found that there was wide variation in costs and success rates. Costs per IVF cycle ranged from £498–£2,546 per cycle excluding drugs and live delivery rates ranged from 8.6% to 18.6% per cycle.

Options for Purchasing a Service

There are basically three options available to a purchasing authority:

1   IVF/GIFT to be considered under formal extra contractual referral (ECR) procedures.

2   Purchasing a service from an existing NHS or private provider.

Within this option there are two possibilities, either purchasing a total service or a co-operative service (transport IVF) with the district providing part of the assessment and treatment stages. Transport IVF involves patients having their initial work up, ie consultation, administration of drugs, ultrasound scans, etc followed by egg collection at the base unit. The collected eggs are then transported to the specialist IVF unit along with the sperm where the embryology is carried out and the patient then attends the specialist unit for embryo transfer two days later.

3   Establishing a new local NHS service for the Authority.

These options were costed and discussed in detail.

Recommendations

By synthesising the information it was possible to make clear recommendations on the nature and level of service to be purchased.

1   The treatment costs of IVF and GIFT are similar. IVF will detect poor fertilisation and can be used to bypass damaged fallopian tubes. GIFT will not detect poor fertilisation but is dependent on the ability to fertilise. It was recommended therefore that IVF and not GIFT be purchased.

2   Between centres there is a wide variation in costs and success rates. It was recommended that Purchasing Officers should negotiate with the named centres identified in the report.

3   The survey of consultants indicated that if there were an easily accessible free service the number of women sent for IVF/GIFT would be approximately twice that of the number of private patients being sent. It was therefore recommended that, in order to complement the level of private service provision, a total of 62 IVF cycles be purchased, to provide a comparable level of NHS service provision, and be available as indicated below:

Brighton/Hove/Lewes: 30 cycles
Eastbourne/Wealden: 16 cycles
Hastings/Rother: 16 cycles

HFEA 1990 data showed that the average number of treatment cycles per patient in the UK was 1.16 cycles. It was recommended therefore that there should be a maximum of two cycles of IVF per patient.

4   It is estimated that the costs of purchasing 62 cycles of IVF is approximately £62,000 but considerable opportunities exist to reduce costs per IVF cycle depending upon the number of cycles purchased.

5   There was some agreement between the consultants surveyed that maternal age and parity should be a barrier. The success of IVF decreases with an increase in maternal age, there is a decrease with women over 40 years old. It was recommended that only women under 40 years old and couples with nil or one child should be considered for IVF.

6   It was recommended that selection for NHS treatment should only be made by the consultants in charge of the subfertility clinics.

7   It was recommended that a working group should be established to produce a shared protocol to determine access to the service.

Letting a Contract

Having determined a budget, based on an estimate of costs and minimum number of cycles needed for the population, a service specification was drawn up and identified units invited to bid for the contract.

Units were asked to submit information on costs, success rates and patient selection for a set period of time to try to ensure that the information was up-to-date and comparable. It was then possible to construct a table which allowed comparison of the units. Table 1 presents the method adopted which allowed costs and success rates per cycle to be taken into consideration by calculating the cost per live delivery. Other costs were also taken into consideration, costs associated with frozen embryo cycles were considered as costs could be greatly reduced if a frozen embryo could be used for a women's second IVF cycle and abandonment of treatment costs were also considered as in some cases the charge was the same as for a completed cycle. Factors other than costs were also important such as travelling distance and time, accessibility and availability of patient support group, etc. All this information was collated and presented to the working group responsible for producing the shared protocol and a decision reached concerning where to place the contract.

Table 1   *Relating costs and success rates for IVF Units*

	Unit A	Unit B	Unit C
Cost Per Cycle	£850	£740	£620
Cost Per 62 Cycles	£52,700	£45,880	£38,440
Live Delivery Rate Per Cycle	20.8%	22.5%	16.7%
Anticipated Deliveries Per 62 Cycles	12.9	14.1	10.3
Anticipated Cost Per Delivery	£4,085	£3,253	£3,732

East Sussex Health Authority subsequently purchased 62 cycles of IVF for 1993/1994.

References

Effective Health Care: The Management of Subfertility, (August 1992) University of Leeds.

Hull M G R, Glazener C M A, Kell N J, Conway D I, Foster P A, Hinton R A, Coulson C, Lamert P A, Watt E M and Desai K M (1985). Population Study of Causes, *Treatment and Outcome of Infertility*. British Medical Journal, 291, 1693–1697.

Address for contact

Cynthia Lyons, Department of Public Health Medicine, East Sussex Health Authority, Westlords, 250 Willingdon Rd, Eastbourne, BN20 9AL.

Cost-Effective Purchasing of Health Care

JENNY MORRIS, ADRIAN BAGUST and JAMES PIERCY, York Health
Economics Consortium

SUMMARY

In April 1991 the York Health Economics Consortium embarked upon a
large scale, innovative cost-effective purchasing project funded by Trent
and Mersey Regional Health Authorities. The aim of the project is to
provide purchasers with information which is relevant locally on the
effects and costs consequent on changes in purchasing decisions in
either the amount or type of service. There are two main elements to the
project. First, the development of guides for purchasers which summar-
ise the epidemiological evidence, the range of interventions available
and typical pathways patients follow through the health care system.
Second, the development of computer based models to quantify the
various activities and costs associated with the treatment of patients
from the point of entry to the health care system until discharge, review
or death. To date, purchasing guides have been published on contracting for service for patients with lung cancer, childhood deafness (OME)
and maternity services. Guides on the management of patients with
asthma and coronary heart disease will be published in September/
October, and with schizophrenia and stroke by the end of 1993.

Introduction

Since the introduction of the NHS reforms, purchasers have been charged with
assessing the health needs of their resident population and allocating
resources to meet as many of those needs as possible. In order to allocate
resources efficiently, purchasers need to consider information on both the costs
and benefits of alternative uses of resources. While the quality of this information will improve over time, it is clear that comparatively little is known
about the costs and benefits of services purchased.

The aim of the project currently being undertaken at the York Health Economics Consortium is to assist purchasers in the decisions regarding which
health care and treatment interventions are most appropriate to the health
needs of the population. For each disease area or client group, the study will:

Figure 1 *Lung Cancer Treatment Paths*

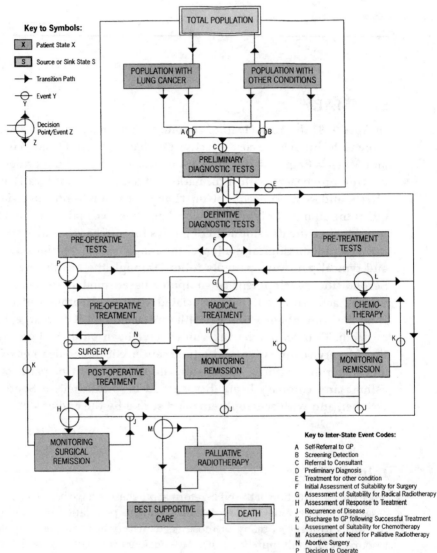

1   Bring together information on resources, quality, outcomes and effectiveness.

2   Provide the basis for purchasers to develop policy and specify contracts.

3   Provide a framework for monitoring and reviewing service contracts.

Method

1   Design

(i)   Identification of disease area/client group.

(ii)   Identify leading research centres and authorities in the study of the disease area and establish working relationships (important for peer review of what is produced and for obtaining information where little exists in the published literature).

(iii) Undertake a literature search to identify:
  - epidemiological information
  - possible range of clinical interventions
  - paths through the health care system
  - clinical effectiveness and cost of interventions

(iv)   Identify key decision points on the care paths, link to available datasets to attach probabilities to the various paths and establish real resource requirements. Figure 1 illustrates the flowpaths for the lung cancer model.

(v)   Construct a computer-based modelling tool to permit a DHA to assess the implications of different strategies using local parameters. Where available national datasets are used. Local data (at DHA level) are entered when the structure of the model is considered robust.

(vi)   Work with DHAs to test applications of the model in local settings. Table 1 illustrates the type of data requested from DHAs for the lung cancer model.

Table 1 *Lung Cancer Model – Data Requirements*

A	**Activity Inputs**

1   Resident population profile – age and sex groups as follows:
< 44, 45–49, 50–54, 55–59, 60–64, 65–69, 70–74, 75–79, 80–84, 85+

2   Either local incidence/mortality rates in age bands or local SMR (and then use national rates).

3   Proportion of referrals for '? lung cancer' who actually have the disease. Either single figure or by age bands.

4   Casemix: small cell and non-small cell.
Percentage distribution between cell types.

5   Death rate at diagnostic stage.

6   Percentage patients selected to undergo best supportive care.
Percentage patients selected to undergo definitive diagnosis.
Percentage patients selected to undergo referral to pre-treatment.

7   Percentage defined as early and late stage.

8   Percentage selected for surgery.

9   Percentage surgical patients failing pre-op tests.

10   Percentage surgical patients undergoing pre-op treatment ⎫ mainly
Percentage surgical patients undergoing post-op treatment ⎪ for
Percentage surgical patients undergoing pre and post-op treatment ⎬ costing
Percentage surgical patients undergoing no pre and post-op ⎪ purpose
treatment ⎭

11   Percentage patients found to be inoperable at time of surgery.

12   Survival parameters set up for each cell following surgery eg monthly death rates for early and late stage survival at 1 year and 5 years for early and late stages.

13   Remission: post-operative remission for those treated surgically (reviewed at 2 months).

14   Assessment for those treated non-surgically:
Percentage selected to undergo radical radiotheraphy ⎫ by early
Percentage selected to undergo chemotherapy ⎬ and late
Percentage selected to undergo best supportive care ⎭ stage

15   Treatment outcome: non-surgical.
Radiotherapy: survival, remission at 6 months.
Chemotherapy: survival, remission at 3 months.
Best supportive care: numbers given palliative radiotherapy; survival.

B	**Cost Inputs (this is the area where most assistance needed from DHAs)**

16   For each activity input, volume and resources per 100 patients.

2   Classification of Information

(i)   Patient focused to document the experience of patients from first contact
       with health care services through to discharge/monitoring/death.

Advantages

- Consistent with the development of programme budgeting
  framework.

- Enables rational planning as it
  becomes obvious which
  elements of care are most
  effective.

- Easier to identify where
  choices about treatment can be
  made.

- Easier to link outcome data for
  patients with multiple episodes (eg lung cancer patients
  can be managed across 4/5
  specialties including block
  medical and surgical
  contracts).

- Costs and outcomes are
  assessed more easily by following patients through the
  system.

Disadvantages

- Currently difficult to match with
  traditional block contracts.

- Difficulty in obtaining logitudi-
  nal datasets.

3   Development of computer models

Computer models are constructed around the network flow diagram for the
disease and aim to represent the numbers of patients in each part of the system
in a typical contract year. At present the models are essentially 'steady-state'
representations, which allow service demand, resource deployment and
health service costs to be estimated and compared between alternative planning scenarios.

4   Areas of study

Lung Cancer
Maternity Services
Childhood Deafness (otitis media with effusion)
Coronary Heart Disease
Asthma
Stroke
Schizophrenia

Application of information

The clinical and cost-effectiveness information is reproduced in the form of a
Purchasers Guide which can be used locally to aid planning of services.

Each guide identifies the key decisions for purchasers, reviews critically the clinical and cost-effectiveness literature, and provides guidance for the contracting process where the data are robust, or highlights areas where further work needs to be undertaken. In the lung cancer documents, for example, the guide is divided into logical sections vis-a-vis management. These include the role of clincial trials, prevention, diagnostic testing and treatment.

The guides are disseminated free of charge to the District Health Authorities in the two funding regions (Trent and Mersey) and are available at cost to other organisations.

The computer models are used by District Health Authorities to firstly describe where resources are currently being directed and, secondly, to model particular 'what if' scenarios. For example, the model for lung cancer could illustrate the consequences of reducing radiotherapy and chemotherapy. For coronary heart disease, it would be possible to model the implications on cost and activity of increasing the rate of surgery.

As well as providing information to help contract specifications, the guides and the outputs from the computer models provide a focus to the dialogue essential to good working relationships between purchasers and providers.

Future Work

- Examine the way in which purchasing guides and computer models can be used in moving towards a system of programme-based contracting and whether additional information is required to support the purchasing function.

- Further testing of the extent to which the computer model and the information contained in the purchaser guides meet the needs of purchasing authorities.

- Together with purchasing authorities, identifying priority areas for future guides and models.

- Development of computer based models to look at 'what-if' scenarios within service areas (eg services for cancer patients in general).

Acknowledgements

This project is funded by Trent and Mersey Regional Health Authorities and we are grateful for their support. We would also like to acknowledge the work of Ian Taylor and his colleagues at Computype in York for producing the artwork for the poster and accompanying figure and table.

Address for contact

Dr Jenny Morris, Research Fellow, York Health Economics Consortium, University of York, Heslington, York, YO1 5DD.

The Assessment of Mental Health Need and its Translation into Policy and Practice

K SNEE, Department of Public Health, Sefton District Health Authority
E CHURCH, Department of Public Health, Mersey Regional Health
Authority
J HOTCHKISS and A MARCHBANK, The Liverpool Public Health
Observatory, Liverpool University

SUMMARY

Often assessment of health need has little impact on policy development and even less upon practice. In order to ensure that action follows
directly from health needs assessment there should be a process that
will not only develop appropriate recommendations but that will
achieve consensus and commitment from practitioners and senior management and an input from consumers. In Chester DHA in 1991/2 a
project was facilitated with the help of the Liverpool Public Health
Observatory (LPHO) that aimed to develop a coherent strategy for the
development of mental health services in Chester based upon the
consensus of professionals and consumers.

Introduction

All too often in health authorities the work of public health departments in the
assessment of need fails to be translated into policy and practice. The purpose
of this short article is to describe an approach which attempts to ensure that
local research is incorporated directly into policy.

Chester DHA was considering the future direction of its psychiatric services –
a model proposed was that of mental health resource centres. There was,
however, no consensus about whether this was the most appropriate way to
develop services and if it was, what form it should take. To ensure that any
development is optimally planned it is important to assess need and achieve a
high degree of consensus about the future direction of the service. The project
aimed to develop a coherent strategy for the development of mental health
services in Chester based upon the consensus of professionals and consumers.
It also attempted to estimate the prevalence of both major and minor psychiatric morbidity in Chester and Ellesmere Port and to determine the perceived
needs of consumers in relation to those mental health needs identified and the
perceived needs and role of primary and secondary health care workers and
relate it to health needs identified.

The study had five main components (Figure 1):

1   Literature review
2   Primary care study
3   Outpatients study
4   Mental Health Care Workers study
5   Workshops

Figure 1 *Study Outline*

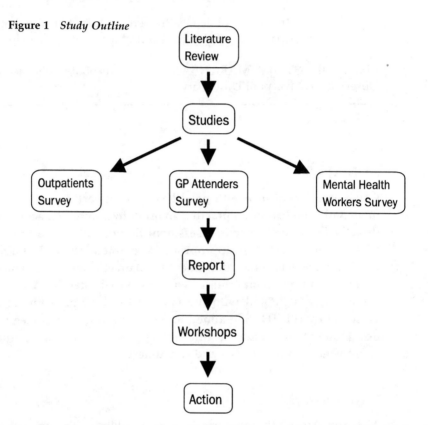

The elements of this approach are therefore to analyse national and local routine data to conduct local research amongst consumers of the service and professionals and then to develop recommendations based upon a consensus conference. The approach to analyse need explicitly took account of the use of resources to maximise health gain (Figure 2):

Figure 2 *Framework for Health Needs*

What is the health status of the population?
eg what is the extent of mental health problems in the population? what is the current service utilisation? etc.

What resources are available?
eg what skills and facilities are available? how much do we spend on service provision? etc.

How may resources be best targeted to maximise health gain?
eg what do local consumers want? what are the most effective treatment and support options? what are national priorities? etc.

There is not space for discussion of the individual studies but the results of the process in terms of the recommendations are summarised below. Many of the recommendations have been implemented or have been developed – some of them of profound significance. For example the refocussing of the service around primary care is taking place. The participative nature of the project has led to a wide ownership and a development of dialogue that is unlikely to have occurred had the project not taken place.

Recommendations

Training

We recommend that a multisectoral task group with user, carer and GP involvement should be established to develop a training strategy for Chester District. It should consider the financial implications, and draw up a job description for a training co-ordinator who will be accountable to the multi-sectoral group.

Community Directory

We recommend that a directory containing a comprehensive breakdown of local NHS, Social Service and voluntary sector resources for mental health be established and updated on a yearly basis.

Multidisciplinary working

We recommend that a task group containing representation from the NHS and Social Services (commissioners and providers), the voluntary sector, Users and General Practice is established to report within 6 months on a strategy to ensure that there will be a common set of records and common database.

Helpline

We recommend that the 24hr helpline should continue for a trial 1 year period and that this should develop according to regular audit of activity. It is important that it is well publicised.

User involvement

We recommend that 'Marketplace' should be allowed to develop a role as an advisory body for operational advice.

We recommend that every service user should have a care plan and that the process should be constructed so that it could inform service development.

We recommend that a task group should consider how user involvement can be extended into the more strategic planning of mental health services. It must be recognised that any extension will carry with it a financial cost to the user and this should be met by the funding agencies.

The Development of Service Structure

We recommend that the concept of sectorisation requires a significant overhaul. If any element of sectorisation is to be retained it should be less rigidly adhered to, especially for inpatients, and should be based around practice populations and not geographical areas. Agreements about the appropriate way to proceed should be reached through the Care Planning Team, the Local Medical Committee and in discussion with GP practices.

We recommend that the Mental Health Service should be developed around and in partnership with local primary health care teams. The development of Mental Health Resource Centres (MHRCs) should only be considered further if they are deemed to be necessary as a result of this process.

Address for contact

Dr Kevin Snee, Consultant in Public Health Medicine, Department of Public Health Medicine, Sefton DHA, Scarsdale Hospital, Newbold Rd, Chesterfield S41 7PF.

Copies of the full report are available from the Liverpool Public Health Observatory, University of Liverpool, Department of Public Health, PO Box 147, Liverpool L69 3BX.

Community Care Implementation: Perspective from the Health Boards in Scotland

JULIE TAYLOR, Social Work Research Centre, University of Stirling

SUMMARY

In depth interviews were conducted with all fifteen Scottish health boards, to provide an overview of implementation of community care within the health sector. Topics covered in the interviews included community care service delivery, health and social care responsibilities, the role of health personnel in assessment and care management arrangements, resource transfer policies, joint funding mechanisms for services, and preparation of discharge protocols. The study aims to give an overview of the policies on community care pursued by health boards and their perspective on areas of joint working with regional councils.

Introduction

As part of a wider study investigating the efficiency and effectiveness of community care, the Social Work Research Centre at the University of Stirling has undertaken in-depth interviews with all Scottish health boards and local authorities. The interviews, in June and July 1993, were designed to provide an overview of implementation of community care within the health and social sector. Topics of interest included the structure for community care service delivery, health and social care responsibilities and the role of health personnel in assessment and care management arrangements. Policies for resource transfers and joint funding mechanisms for community care services were also explored, together with the progress which has been made in the preparation of discharge protocols. The main findings, with respect to health boards, are summarised below.

Organisational and operational aspects of community care service delivery

There is a rapid expansion of the number of provider units applying for Trust status across Scotland. Initially the uptake was slow, with the health minister setting the relatively low target of two Trusts by 1992. Although only two boards have full Trust status for all their provider units at present, a further five predict they will do so by April 1994. With the exception of the Island boards, where there is some doubt whether trust status will ever be viable, the remaining boards expect to do so by 1995.

The shift towards Trusts as opposed to directly managed units brings with it the question of how far protocols or agreements already reached with local authorities apply to units and trusts. Health board responses to the issue differed markedly. For example, some adopt a 'bottom up' approach, with the provider units developing protocols independently, whilst others rely on service agreements to ensure protocols are accepted.

Health boards were asked to identify where the main responsibility for community care was located within their organisation. The responses varied greatly, ranging from those who specified planning mechanisms such as the strategic planning team, to those who could not identify any one individual or group. A small number of boards had created specific community care posts whilst others identified named individuals such as the director of planning and development.

Although research has endorsed the value of locating social workers within hospitals (Connor & Tobbitt, 1988), there is a clear trend across Scotland towards reducing the numbers based in hospitals or even withdrawing whole teams. The majority of boards expressed concern at this development. In addition, some felt that they had not been part of the dialogue regarding the future of hospital social work which added to their uncertainty regarding the eventual outcome of this issue.

Arrangements for Assessment and Care Management

There are currently very few examples of health care staff acting as care managers. However, in principle, boards were generally keen to adopt a care management role where appropriate, particularly in the field of learning disabilities or mental health. Only in one area was a joint agency model of care management and assessment in operation although three others were currently considering this option.

In relation to assessment, health care professionals retain the responsibility for assessing health care needs and are closely involved in giving assessment and referral information.

Collaboration

Community Care Plans: Health Boards were universally in favour of producing joint plans, with most planning to do so by 1995. In addition there is evidence of a shift from region-wide to locality based plans.

Health and Social Care Boundaries: Health boards were generally more circumspect than their local authority planning partners in their perceptions of progress achieved in agreeing policies. Most indicated that in the main the detail of their respective responsibilities have yet to be defined.

Joint Data Bases: Although there are isolated examples of initiatives, there is little evidence to indicate any real progress in establishing joint data bases.

Routine collaboration on the important tasks of information gathering and sharing is not yet in place.

Registration and Inspection: The majority of health boards reported some co-operative activity with regard to developing joint standards, quality assurance and contract specifications. Four boards are considering operating joint teams.

Other Agencies: While health board links with primary health, housing and voluntary agencies are reasonably well established, collaborative mechanisms with the private sector are considerably less developed.

Hospital Admission and Discharge Arrangements

The majority of health boards have produced agreements/protocols relating to long-stay discharge arrangements, however, evidence of joint collaboration in the production of discharge plans was rare. Generally, care programme planning has developed separately from that of care management.

Very few acute admission and discharge arrangements had been agreed. Whilst most boards reported 'work in progress' some were clearly close to completion whilst for others discussions were only just starting to get underway.

Resource Transfers and Contracting

With one exception, all boards either have projects currently operating under the bridging finance scheme or were in the process of preparing bids for this year's round. Bridging finance projects were considered to be prime candidates for permanent resource transfers.

Target setting for resource transfers by the NHS management executive posed problems in terms of coordinating planning. Most boards, under pressure to achieve their objectives, reported difficulties coordinating with the local authorities' timescales. This in part was echoed by the local authorities, most of which found reaching agreements with health boards on the issue of resource transfers problematic. In addition, calculating net savings was a task considered difficult by most boards, with at least one attempting to simplify the process by developing a standardised methodology for estimating the net reduction in overall running costs.

Just under half of all health boards had agreements with local authorities relating to commissioning and contracting of community care services. Most boards favoured bi-lateral contracts although the exact detail had yet to be negotiated. Competitive tendering was in the early stages of being developed. Of the boards who were considering this option, a preference for selective tendering from known providers was expressed.

Note

1. This paper draws upon work completed by colleagues at the Social Work Research Centre – Alison Petch and Kirsten Stalker. Their invaluable contribution is gratefully acknowledged.

Reference

Connor, A and Tobbitt, J E (1988). *Social Workers and Health Care in Hospital.* Central Research Unit, Social Work Services Group, Scottish Office.

Address for contact

Julie Taylor, Social Work Research Centre, University of Stirling, STIRLING FK9 4LA.

An Examination of Specialty Costs: Incorporating the Effects of Case-mix

RICHARD C WILSON & MARK S GILTHORPE, Institute of Public & Environmental Health, The University of Birmingham

SUMMARY

Contracts, costs and management systems are associated with specialties, whilst the epidemiology of needs assessment and health gain is centred upon diseases. Therefore, if costs are to be understood in relation to morbidity, a mapping of aetiologically-grouped diseases to specialties is required.

A diseases-to-specialty mapping could be constructed from any relevant data set, but the concern of this study is hospital in-patient activity which consumes more resources than any other aspect of health care. Such maps are important in understanding the way in which changing patterns of disease will impact on resource use within hospitals.

The methodology developed will enable the monitoring of in-patient activity within district specialty groups and validate that activity with respect to the Region. Upon this basis studies will embrace the concept of deprivation and include financial data, to facilitate the evaluation of actual resource use by each district specialty.

1 Aim

In the NHS, contracts, costs and management systems are associated with specialties defined in terms of patient characteristics or methods of treatment, whilst the epidemiology of needs assessment and health gain is centred upon diseases. This dichotomy can lead to differing categorisations of a disease in different locations, creating a range of specialty 'case-mixes'. Case-mix in the context of this paper refers to the mix of disease conditions coded to specialties. Therefore, before any attempt can be made to reconcile cost to morbidity, a mapping of disease-to-specialty is required. Once a suitable disease-to-specialty mapping has been carried out it is possible to examine the quality of data used and to produce data which have been adjusted for case-mix by indirect standardisation.

The allocation of resources is apportioned by population measures, and in this capitation based system, episode-costing is all important. This paper demonstrates how one source of costs – the financial return – can be used to produce a 'rough-and-ready estimate' of resource use within the Region and how resource use is related to specialties.

2   Materials

Activity data:

All in-patient finished consultant episodes (FCEs) in the West Midlands Regional Health Authority (WMRHA) for the financial year 1991–92 were extracted from the WMRHA Regional Information System (RIS).

Financial data:

Expenditure on in-patient FCEs by specialty was extracted from financial return 22 (FR22) as submitted by each provider unit (including Trusts). The FR22 is a derivative of the old FR12. The use of contract prices was initially considered but had to be excluded for three reasons: 1, Contract prices are set specific to the type of admission and booking agency, adding another degree of complexity to an already complicated mapping procedure; 2, Contract prices are infrequently set against a background of true episode cost and therefore do not reflect true expenditure; 3, Contract prices are not exhaustive whereas the FR22s are and they provide complete coverage of all Korner specialties across the Region.

Figure 1 shows the age-specific trends for in-patient activity and financial data for the Regional population. There are two interesting factors to note in the profiles: the high contribution of the under 5 year-olds and the over 65 year-olds in resource use, reflecting the larger expenditure required within these age groups.

3   Methods

The use of disease-to-specialty mapping allows the standardisation of case-mix and therefore accounts for the variations in coding practices and referral patterns employed across the Region. The RIS data is tabulated by disease group, specialty, age, sex and district into a matrix. A Regional episode rate is calculated by dividing each cell in the matrix by the total Regional population. Multiplying each cellular episode rate by the district population produces the expected activity for every district, which is then summed up for the Region. The age-sex and case-mix Standardised Episode Ratio (SER) is then calculated from the observed and expected activity.

By using this model it is possible to indirectly standardise for material deprivation by expanding the matrix to include Townsend or any other suitable stratified index.

Figure 1 *The age profiles of in-patient activity and expenditure in WMRHA for 1991/92.*

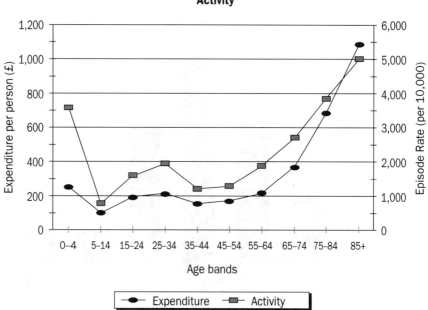

Age-Specific rates of Expenditure and Activity

4 Episode-costing

The investigation of the FR22s was carried out to produce an episode cost for each specialty for each provider unit. These would be summed up to produce DHA and Regional costings. This aim was not immediately realisable due to problems encountered with the FR22s. Initially it was believed that the FR22 would contain accurate data on activity and expenditure, unfortunately only the recorded expenditure stood up to any examination. Several of the FR22 forms were missing either bed days or FCEs, some were even missing both. By comparing the patterns of activity on the FR22 with RIS it was decided that the activity fields should be re-created using RIS 'to fill in the gaps'. This has produced some 'realistic' values for episode costings at the Regional level. It is hoped that the second generation of FR22s being collected currently will be more reliable and provide a greater depth of costings.

5 Results

The distribution of average all-causes FCE cost amongst the districts is shown in Figure 2, and listed in Table 1. The average FCE cost ranges from £683.23 to £2165.29 with a mean of £1231.49 and a standard deviation of £434.80.

The average FCE costs derived have proved, in general, to be pretty robust. Table 2 lists the average FCE cost for each specialty. Those flagged with an asterisk in the table were either not present in the RIS data, ie Clinical

Figure 2 *The distribution of average FCE cost (all causes) amongst districts in the West Midlands RHA.*

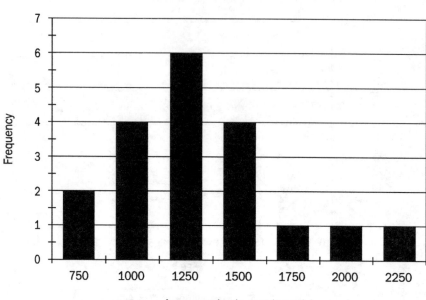

Distribution of average FCE cost across DHAs

Average episode cost (pounds)

Table 1 *The Average FCE cost for each District in WMRHA as derived in this study*

District	Code	Average FCE cost (all causes) in pounds
Hereford	M02	1,148.43
Worcestershire	M04	977.54
Shropshire	M05	1,123.52
Mid Staffs	M06	683.23
North Staffs	M07	1,340.31
South East Staffs	M08	1,044.53
South Warwickshire	M11	1,256.09
East Birmingham	M13	953.69
North Birmingham	M14	1,510.01
West Birmingham	M16	1,265.43
Coventry	M17	1,159.40
Dudley	M18	1,349.49
Sandwell	M19	702.58
Solihull	M20	939.22
Walsall	M21	1,951.60
Wolverhampton	M22	1,174.73
North East Warwickshire	M24	819.11
South Birmingham	M25	2,165.29
North Worcestershire	M26	1,146.31
Region	M23	1,231.49

Table 2 *The Regional average FCE cost for each FR22 specialty as derived in this study*

Specialties	Specialty Number	Average Episode Cost (in Pounds)	Standard Deviation	Flagged Values
Paediatrics	1	522.78	362.95	
Geriatrics	2	3,225.76	1,508.36	
Cardiology	3	1,267.68	1,297.39	
Dermatology	4	808.52	1,569.08	
Infectious Diseases	5	1,129.51	1,659.46	
Medical Oncology	6	2,720.98	3,276.81	
Neurology	7	1,478.87	1,706.38	
Rheumatology	8	1,955.33	3,260.31	
Gastroenterology	9	556.58	7,042.77	
Haematology (Clinical)	10	589.19	635.63	
Clinical Immunology and Allergy	11	0.00	n/a	*
Thoracic Medicine	12	1,022.67	17,534.37	
Genito-Urinary Medicine	13	212.48	177.39	
Nephrology	14	101.89	180.89	
Rehabilitation Medicine	15	73,693.46	7,060.82	*
Other Medical	16	916.08	423.73	
General surgery	17	1,336.52	1,313.16	
Urology	18	747.73	504.82	
Orthopaedics	19	1,492.01	549.30	
ENT	20	606.89	390.12	
Ophthalmology	21	841.94	1,015.89	
Gynaecology	22	554.62	261.89	
Dental Specialties	23	721.04	405.53	
Neurosurgery	24	2,624.38	4,391.98	
Plastic surgery	25	1,112.10	1,303.07	
Cardiothoracic surgery	26	2,347.86	2,845.27	
Paediatric surgery	27	1,913.11	1,667.84	
Obstetrics	28	777.78	417.83	
General Practice	29	237.72	227.64	
Mental handicap	30	8,515.09	19,695.28	*
Mental illness	31	5,254.72	5,929.22	
Child and adolescent psychiatry	32	20,069.97	23,697.18	*
Forensic psychiatry	33	59,434.65	33,907.27	*
Psychotherapy	34	153,748.40	55,847.42	*
Old Age psychiatry	35	10,922.60	529,695.25	*
General Practice (not maternity)	36	0.00	n/a	*
Radiotherapy	37	1,053.10	1,121.38	

Table 2—continued

Specialties	Specialty Number	Average Episode Cost (in Pounds)	Standard Deviation	Flagged Values
Pathology specialties and radiology	38	1,188.32	21,250.37	
Anaesthetics	39	429.71	528.98	
A and E	40	403.16	778.92	
Regional Average Cost per episode		1,231.49	434.80	

Figure 3 *The predicted expenditure for each specialty is derived using the Regional average FCE cost. This value is then deducted from the actual specialty expenditure, to reveal greater resource use in the long stay specialties.*

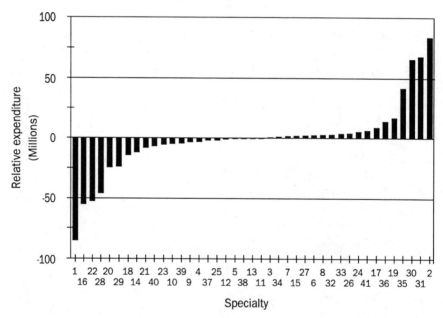

Immunology and General Practice (other than maternity) or those with problems related to coding ie the Mental Health specialties. From a disease-to-specialty mapping carried out on the RIS data, the mental health specialties consistently showed in the top ten percent of 'miscoded' specialties (Institute of Public and Environmental Health, 1993). These miscoded specialties were those whose activity differed relative to that of the Regional norm. In the case of the Mental Health specialties this was due in particular to the treatment of medical conditions not associated with mental illness in long stay patients.

The other noticeable aspect of the table is the presence of large standard deviations. This phenomenon is not novel and it has been observed in more localised studies (Bell, 1987). Whether or not such averages are acceptable is open to debate. Some have argued that such broad brush estimates, like the ones used here, should not prevent trade as they are sufficient for setting prices (Robinson, 1990). It is expected that with a more detailed investigation of RIS activity, the variance will be reduced when corrections are made for locally observed differences, as highlighted in the disease-to-specialty map.

Using the average FCE cost for the Region it is possible to plot an actual vs expected expenditure for each specialty (Figure 3). This figure illustrates the problem of long stay specialties on resource use. The top four resource intensive specialties are Geriatrics and Mental Health. It is important that any allocation of resources takes these particular problems into account, since expenditure on Geriatric care amounts to 11.29% of all Regional in-patient expenditure, but only 4.3% of activity. Mental Health specialties similarly account for 18.86% of expenditure and 3.19% of activity.

6   Discussion

This work has been hampered by inconsistencies in both the activity and financial data sets. We have tried to reduce these as far as possible by de-selecting erroneous data, removing from the investigation those episodes which have no known district of residency, sex, age, or specialty code. By using the method outlined above it has been possible to produce some relevant observations concerning resource use in specialties, in particular the continuing problem of the high resource use of long stay and elderly patients. In doing so more questions have been raised than answered. Costs in the NHS are still in an evolutionary stage. The introduction of market forces will eventually see a levelling out of episode costs. Until such a time, the allocation of resources will have to be finely balanced against a background of compounding influences on episode cost variations. In particular the combined effects of demography, socio-economic factors and patient characteristics need to be firmly understood before prices can be more accurately set and interpreted.

Acknowledgements

One of the authors (Richard Wilson) wishes to express gratitude to the West Midlands Regional Health Authority for financial support.

References

Bell R (1987). Modelling the costs of Heart transplants by Patient Characteristics: A perspective on DRGs. **HERG Discussion paper No. 5**, Brunel University.

Robinson R (1990). Competition and health care. **Research Report No. 6**, Kings Fund Institute, London.

Institute of Public and Environmental Health (1993). A Preliminary study into an epidemiological model for cost evaluation of hospital in-patient activity. **IPEH Working Paper**, University of Birmingham.

Address for contact

Mr Richard Wilson, Institute of Public & Environmental Health, Medical School, The University of Birmingham, Edgbaston, Birmingham, B15 2TT.

Questions and Discussion

Below are edited excerpts of the principal points raised during the question and discussion sessions of the conference.

Peter Brooks (Director of Public Health and Planning, Herefordshire HA)
Could I ask Peter Smith about the effect on hospital activity he mentioned in relation to population density, and the extent to which that may be distorted by aggregation to synthetic wards? We have a large number of extremely sparsely populated wards and therefore much of our population may be, in effect, lost in your analysis.

Peter Smith (Department of Economics, University of York)
They wouldn't be lost. Most populations would be aggregated with other wards so that the minimum unit size is 5,000. That was the decision we made. The wards are contiguous and all lie within the same local authority. We think the density variable is reflecting the rural position, and I don't think the fact that sparsely populated areas are aggregated with less sparsely populated areas is going to cause much of a problem. If you have any area that is sparsely populated it will be picked up as sparsely populated and remain so within our analysis.

Madhavi Bajekal (Department of General Practice, St Mary's Hospital Medical School)
Peter Smith mentioned they had got a very high R squared with their model. Have you done a similar analysis with the old RAWP review formula? Secondly, we have also used a very crude measure for GP access and have found it to be non significant in explaining variation. What was the GP measure that you used? Finally, are you suggesting that the allocation formula be determined at ward level?

Peter Smith
I would say our method is different to the review of RAWP in that we have used a more satisfactory statistical methodology. In our model we are not seeking to explain as much of the variance as we can. If we were, we would just bring in more and more variables. We were just using the variables that we had identified as being important in determining utilisation and what I am reporting is that those variables account for 49% of utilisation in a very large dataset (nearly 5,000 wards).

Our GP access variable also is very crude, simply the number of GPs in an area and the distance to them. It is like the hospital access measure.

Do we allocate to wards? We have looked at the implications of allocating money for the wards and then adding up the wards to get the district's total and then the region's. Quite frankly, we don't find it makes much difference whether you allocate straight to the district or if you allocate to the wards and then sum to the districts. Of course that might change depending on whatever formula you finally arrive at and we will of course test that.

Roger Dewhurst (Director of Information Services, Mersey RHA)
One of the things that worried me about Professor Jarman's method of allocating resources is allocating to GP fundholders and the issues raised by the ecological fallacy. Essentially we are talking about approaches that allocate resources to populations. You make assumptions, particularly at ward level, that average area characteristics apply to the GP lists. For example, that all the people in a ward with certain social characteristics are registered with one practice, and people with another set of social characteristics are registered with another practice.

Brian Jarman (Department of General Practice, St Mary's Hospital Medical School)
Geoff Royston and others have said the ecological fallacy is a bit of a red herring and I think there is something in this statement. I think the more important issue is the inappropriateness of using the average ward SMR for the GP population within that ward.

Rob Cooper (Director of Public Health, Solihull Health Authority)
Whatever resource allocation formula is developed it needs to be robust down to small population sizes, such as those of fundholder practices of about 7,000. My concern is that if you incorporated SMR 0–74, this would not be the case. I think that it is essential to look at the service needs of any formula that is developed. However, in the meantime, I would suggest that we use only those variables which are robust down to small population sizes such as the GP fundholder practices.

Peter Smith
I certainly think that we would share your concern at using the allocation model we have derived down to that small population level. We are fairly confident that the models would be okay at a district level, but if the GP fundholding allocation problem is becoming as important as it seems to be I think our view would be that you cannot escape the need for cohort studies, following individuals and their health care requirements. We are also looking at a way of resourcing GP fundholders in the interim, but we haven't really got far with that as yet.

Rod Griffiths (Institute of Public & Environmental Health, University of Birmingham)
But somebody is actually going to have to allocate the resources to fundholders next April, and the April after that. If you don't have an allocation formula that handles the fundholders and the districts the same, you are putting a time bomb in every district. With my academic hat on, of course let us do many, many cohort studies, preferably as expensive as possible, but in the meantime the treasurers are going to have to allocate the money. At the moment there are enormous tensions in the system and a wide spread belief

that it would be wrong to have different allocation systems. Perhaps when we have all been able to see the full York University report we will all have to bend our minds, as Rob suggested, to find ways in which something can be invented that will work for fundholders as well. In the reformed health service it is not clear whose job that is going to be.

Nick Webb (Director of Finance, Walsall Health Authority)
How quickly is this work likely to be taken on board by the Department of Health?

Peter Dick (Project Leader, Operational Research, NHS Management Executive)
The intention is to use the new formula for 1995/96 for districts, but a different formula will be developed for fundholder practices. That was the intention before the recent government announcement about the abolition of Regional Health Authorities (October 1993). There is certainly no suggestion that the formula that Peter Smith has been talking about will automatically be applied to fundholders.

Anita Bird (Economic Adviser, Operational Research, NHS Management Executive)
The intention is to have a formula which is consistent for fundholders, but fundholders buy a subset of procedures only and so may have different needs driving them compared to the complete volume of acute episodes which the York formula has looked at. So it is perfectly plausible and legitimate that a different relationship for the subset of elective procedures may emerge.

Jim Paris (Medical Adviser, Coventry Family Health Services Authority)
I was particularly struck by Estelle Gilman's work which aggregates wards across the West Midlands, and perhaps takes out of the relationship the effect of differences in GP referral habits. As a Medical Adviser in the West Midlands, I am only too aware of the enormous variation at the gate keeping level of the utilisation of particular resources. Is there not a danger of bias being produced by not acknowledging the activities of GPs? There is now evidence emerging with fundholders, that their utilisation levels are much reduced when they begin to look closely at their activities.

Anita Bird
Has Philip Milner looked at the relationship between provision of services and hospital utilisation or does he feel it would be more appropriate to allocate resources through the Community and Family Health Care services? I wonder whether some of the variation he found reflects differences in the appropriate provision of those services rather than differences in the provision of the secondary care services.

Philip Milner (Director of Public Health, Rotherham Health Authority)
Yes, but on the other hand much of what we do in the Hospital and Community Health side is targeted at depression, respiratory conditions and so on. Clearly what you say needs to be brought into the whole debate of funding health services for a given community, so that we are not parcelling the money up as if this is for FHSAs and this is HCHS.

Andrew Harris (Clinical Director, Lambeth, Southwark & Lewisham FHSA)
If we continue to allocate resources based on what is being used we will tend to perpetuate provider led practices, which purchasers ought to be challenging. Shouldn't we be moving towards setting priorities in a different way? Perhaps we should be asking consumers what they want.

Philip Milner

We have to get to some concept of a national budget for health services across family health services and hospital and community health services, and then allocate down to smaller areas. You could allow the consumer voice to play its part at the local level, for example in determining whether the resources go to hospital and community health services or the family health services, for different types of condition. Essentially I think it is a question of programme budgeting and judgement about how much goes into which aspect of the service and what clinical or health service area. No amount of statistical analysis will untangle these political decisions.

Andrew Harris

Professor Jarman highlighted how crucial the population figures are, and the implications are obvious particularly in allocating resources for fundholders. It seems to me this important question can only be resolved if resources are allocated to make the FHSA lists as accurate as possible. There are so many disincentives at present in the system that actually discourage the accurate keeping of this population base.

It also seems to me an extraordinary paradox that we are talking about resource allocation here which is so tied into activity when purchasers are being pushed to purchase on the basis of *effectiveness* and on the basis of *appropriateness*. Yet there is no measure of either of these in anything I have heard today.

Brian Jarman

We can predict that, by 1995, half of the population will be covered by GP fundholders, in some regions the proportion will be higher. So the quality of the list size data becomes more important, increasingly so as we get further and further away from the census. I think it would be better to try and get the population via the GP lists, particularly with the problems of under-enumeration in the 1991 census. You can improve the accuracy of the GP lists through the FHSAs who can check, by letter, the validity of the lists. Of course, GPs are responsible for all the patients who are living in their area who haven't yet joined their list if they are an emergency, which may be a problem.

Rod Griffiths

The Department of Health consistently refuses to put anything to do with effectiveness into the so called 'efficiency index'. So buying lots more of something that doesn't work gets you lots of brownie points. They have a belief that it is possible to have a *policy neutral* efficiency index. This assumes that all activity works, and it doesn't.

Roger Dewhurst

There is another important issue around what costs to use. What is implicit, if not explicitly stated, in all the resource allocation models, is that we should be moving towards purchasing care at equal prices. The national formula implicitly recognises the price effect in that it acknowledges the London weighting and the effects of market forces.

Rod Griffiths
One of the issues we haven't yet discussed is whether deprived populations or populations with different social characteristics have a different case mix, and whether that case mix has the same set of costs. This may also be a factor in the costs of care in rural areas where costs may be higher because of transport problems or increased lengths of stay. Equally in deprived urban populations there may be a different set of costs because you can't get people out of hospital quickly because they don't have the social facilities or support. I think some differential costings may be justified while others may not, and I am not sure what the trick is to produce the right pressure on prices. I am not convinced that you can simply allocate at the local price levels because that seems to remove any kind of pressure on prices which there ought to be. But, equally, I am not completely convinced that a neutral, national set of costs would work either because of, for example the differential lengths of stay we have seen in our region in areas of different social circumstances.

Brian Jarman
I think there is an implied understanding in all of the resource allocations, that we are all buying at equal prices. Certainly at the regional level, the national formula is constructed as if the prices were the same across the country. I think this is again a major problem, for instance, in all inner city areas. Ultimately we should try to get to equal prices in the allocation for the purchasers, but when provider hospitals have inevitably higher cost to do with such things as teaching, London weighting and so on, that extra cost should be adjusted for at the provider end. So if teaching hospitals have inevitably higher costs, with each cost per case being, let us say 10% higher, the compensation for this should be at the provider end. You can't compensate at the purchaser end, because if you gave the purchasers more for using the teaching hospitals in that area, they would just buy the care from another hospital.

Nick Webb
With respect to Andrew Richardson's paper regarding the interplay of objectivity and subjectivity in resource allocation, I would contend that there is an iterative process, as the objective and technical side of the health needs assessment process must influence the political process. It is not a case simply of there being either subjective *or* objective issues, the important point is the relationship between them.

Andrew Richardson (Consultant in Public Health Medicine, Worcester & District HA)
In my presentation, for clarity, I portrayed objectivity and subjectivity as two dimensions to health, but I agree it is an iterative process. There is a danger that the subjective element is obscured by the 'numbers' and the apparent surety of the technical and epidemiological issues. An analogy can be taken from the Law where Parliament writes the laws which set the policy framework, whilst the courts make the judgements based on evidence within the law – as the technical side of the process. However there is a feedback loop as the decisions made in the courts set precedents and influence future law making.

Rosemary Geller (Director of Public Health, Shropshire HA)
In health needs assessment in Public Health, I would agree that we concentrate on the epidemiological, technical side. However my feeling is that, although not explicitly, implicitly the political dimension is having more influence over what we purchase and provide. This political influence may not be as democratic as we might wish, but historically there has been a strong political dimension.

Andrew Richardson
As Public Health doctors, we have ideological and philosophical values which we would like to be heard. Yet in terms of exercising technical skills, life is much easier if someone tells you 'we want equity of health' or 'equity of access' and we try to achieve that. So we are caught between the two dimensions.

Ken Taylor (Physician, West Birmingham HA)
I would like to make the assertion that poverty, lack of education, unemployment, poor housing, are the things that lead to bad health. Bad health meaning higher perinatal mortality, higher mental illness, higher suicide rates, more cardiovascular disease and more malignant disease. These are the realities that I see every day as a practising physician and I think that the challenge for the researchers is to come up with a formula that will help me in looking after my patients. There is no doubt that these diseases will stay with us until some of the major issues in our society are addressed. Better housing, better education, these are the things that are going to lead us to better health. In the meantime people like me and the general practitioners have got to pick up the consequences of the sort of society that we live in.

Bobbie Jacobson (Director of Public Health, East London & The City HA)
I am sure that all of us have thought about the point that you raise and particularly those of us who are involved in promoting public health, when we know that most of health is gained or lost outside the Health Service. I think there is still a bit of a false dichotomy between what the Health Service picks up and what other Government departments, including those in Europe, will decide in terms of the future health of our nation. I actually think that every health professional, everyone in health authorities, FHSAs and right across the health service, has a small contribution to make. Researchers too have their own contribution to make in the fields in which they operate.

Rod Griffiths
What we really don't know is what it is that causes the problem. I don't know whether there really are more people that are ill in some districts, or whether less are in primary care than in hospital and therefore, if you had more money, you should spend it on the hospital services or on primary care. Another important issue about these allocation formulae is that they are essentially reactive. We need to put extra money into the system somewhere in order to remove the relationship between poverty and health, in other words get the line flat. I suspect we actually need another chunk of money to allocate pro-actively on experimental projects that are designed to change the picture, as well as trying to get equity into the big block allocations.

Ken Buckingham (Health Economist, Cornwall & Isles of Scilly Health Authority)

The issue of how to meet different individuals' perception of their own needs, raised in Andrew Richardson's presentation, has not really been addressed.

Rod Griffiths

That is certainly a problem. I remember doing some work on child health clinics in Birmingham where we asked people how long they waited, and whether or not this was a problem. The people from the well off areas said they waited a quarter of an hour and it was a problem, while the people from the poor areas said they waited three quarters of an hour and it was no problem. So, if we simply ask people if there is a problem, in this example we would have ended up putting more resources into the well off areas where all the children were probably pretty fit anyway. I don't know what the answer is, but I am not being totally trivial when I suggest that we should ask the rich what they want, and give it to the poor. I think what we need is some intelligent use of consumer feedback. Having worked on the Community Health Council for a while I am aware that there is much wisdom there that we should be making better use of.

Bobbie Jacobson

There is a bit of a problem about that which anybody who has tried to do representative surveys of local communities will know. When you ask fairly open questions about what are people's major health needs in the inner city, the answers you get are; cleaning the rubbish off the streets, reducing the risk of violence and improving the housing. Indeed when you do a rather more closed and structured assessment of need within say the mental health field, the most significant unmet needs are for appropriate housing. So there are problems about asking the community because you then get answers that you can't do anything about.

Andrew Harris

The whole scheme of measuring needs seems to be based on increasingly sophisticated and unsatisfactory measures of activity in secondary care, when actually the need is out there in the community. Given, as Professor Jarman says, 90% of the variation is explained by population size, we need to look at what measures we can take in primary care to change the other 10%. In the first instance, why can't we just use smoking prevalence as a means to allocate resources? The data are already beginning to be collected in general practices. What is the data being collected on smoking, asthma, diabetes being used for if not to inform resource allocation?

Sumathi Sundram (Director of Finance, Suffolk Family Health Services Authority)

The health service is funded for all of secondary and primary care yet all the formulae we have looked at today have been mainly based on hospital and acute services. There does seem to be a perverse incentive to keep the status quo, so how can we carry out the objective sent to us from the centre, in terms of moving the services from the secondary sector to primary care services?

Jim Paris

What we need to do is to step back and decide if we need a major change to shift resources into primary care. This would need to take place over a measured length of time so I suspect that we would need to spend twice the amount for a year or two while we ran down the amount of resources spent on secondary care. As I understand it, within Industry that's what you expect to do when major changes occur, you spend more money before you achieve your return. I think perhaps we are approaching this from an unrealistic angle and we are not going to change anything unless we take a very much more radical view.

Brian Jarman

It is difficult to measure what we want to get back. For example we could look for lower death rates. In terms of what we eventually do, people have got to be treated and health can't be measured in the end in terms of lower death rates alone. For some 15 years now I have wondered, as a GP, how much of what I do makes any difference to people's health. Obviously there is a relationship between income and their disabilities, and that is why we developed a social security benefits programme 10 years ago. You can't give people more money but you can help to make sure that people claim their full benefits in this very complex system, and bring their income up to the minimum level. An interesting graph is one of SMR plotted against income. It shows a J shaped curve, with a slight upturn at the higher income end when we drink too much! At the low income end, if you increase income just a little bit the SMR drops very rapidly.

Nick Webb

One implicit assumption in the discussion so far is that the size of the total cake is big enough for what is needed to be done, and all we are discussing is how to divide it up. That is all very well, but if we succeed in shifting resources from secondary to primary care all we may succeed in doing is a degree of rationing. I am not trying to say that the budget is short by any particular amount but I think there is a danger in trying to achieve a perfect world scenario to get this fomula right, which will mean that everybody has the right amount of money to spend. But that isn't necessarily relevant if there isn't the right amount of money in the system in the first place.

Rod Griffiths

The Government would say that in the run up to the last election it threw vast amounts of money at the health services. But where did it go and what did it do? The obvious thing was to go on doing more acute activities. If you have more acute beds, you do more acute activity. If you close them down, length of stay shortens, and patient turn around increases. We actually do very well considering the amount of money we spend compared to other countries, particularly if you take the age structure of this country into account in comparison to places like Canada, America or Japan. Our population is relatively more elderly than almost everybody except the Dutch and the Scandinavians. But if we spent more money on health in this country we would not put it strategically into primary care. We know we wouldn't because we didn't.

130

A separate point I would like to raise is how simple does a resource allocation formula have to be? On one hand we have research intent on trying to sort out the spending pattern, and therefore the formula gets more and more complicated. We also have a previous political view imposed as well, saying the formula has got to be fairly simple. Is there a view on this?

Anita Bird
Can I separate out here how complex the research has to be to deliver a relatively simple formula, because you can do very complex research to deliver a simple formula that checks out in terms of robustness. If complex research is robust research then I think you want complex research and you don't want to limit research. It may require a very complex piece of analysis to deliver a simple result. If we always emphasise simplicity there is a danger that we will stop researchers using the techniques that are the most appropriate. But they do have to present the results of their research in a way that is understandable.

Stephen Munday (Consultant in Public Health Medicine, North Birmingham Health Care Purchasing Consortium)
The formula needs to be simple but not simplistic. Particularly we need to look at what sort of services are more appropriately funded by different mechanisms. From the data I showed, different types of situations require different sorts of data to resolve them (eg services for people with learning difficulties, HIV/AIDS services).

Andrew Harris
It is important that the formula is perceived to be equitable, particularly between GP fundholders' and non GP fundholders' patients. We are in a situation where there is negative equity developing for non fundholder patients. This is going to be absolutely impossible to handle. Whatever formula is produced needs to be tested in a way that we can see, understand and accept. It seems to be a very tall order to get this done for next April.

Rod Griffiths
Districts are also getting bigger and the implications of the new reform system is that they are going to get bigger still. That means that an awful lot of the current inequities will be absorbed into larger districts. We may get to a point where the variation inside districts is actually bigger than the variation between districts. It means that districts have to start examining how they are putting their money on the ground. It is very much easier to ignore a pocket of deprivation when it is buried inside a rich district, than when it is all together in a district like West Birmingham.

Bobbie Jacobson
Surely the sub district allocation you describe is all about commissioning for health benefit. We are all encouraged to shift resources towards greater health benefit, although there is no evidence yet that we are succeeding. Could I just bring back the discussion to the point you made earlier about ear marking, or reserving, particular resources to achieve particular purposes. This is beginning to happen at district level. Interestingly, it happened first in many of the inner city districts that have been capitation losers because the purchasers realised quite quickly that unless they started to shift resources in a positive

way, intended future changes would never happen. Some of the biggest resource losers are those in London who have created health gain funds. These are ideas that are perhaps not necessarily based on a great deal of science, but the idea is to take a bit of money from everywhere and make sure that the allocation of that money is directed towards what are local priorities.

Madhavi Bajekal
Perhaps there should be some relationship between health targets and funding in order to provide an incentive for action and for progress.

Rod Griffiths
I have always felt that we should take the SMR out of the allocation process. If there is no connection between what we do and the SMR then why are we doing it, and if there is why are we giving health authorities money for killing people? I realise the issues are not that simple, but it does seem to me that there is a circular argument in using the SMR for allocation purposes. If we could find some other method I would feel a lot more comfortable, because we could then put the SMR into the performance review side. We could then ask the question – if we've given you all this money why aren't you saving lives? At the end of the day that's why we have the money.

Roger Dewhurst
Some interesting work has been done by Manchester University for the Department of Environment, in relationship to the construction of a deprivation index. They found that SMR was a preferred variable, even to long term limiting illness, in terms of explaining differences between areas. Logically I accept your argument, but in other areas people are saying that SMR is a very good proxy variable.

Karen Hancock (Economic Adviser, Scottish Office NHSME)
An alternative hypothesis is that not enough is being given in relation to SMR and that the SMR should have a larger weighting factor, say a factor of two.

Vera Carstairs (National Co-ordinator, Health Services Research Networks, University of Edinburgh)
One topic we haven't touched on today is the use of avoidable mortality and morbidity, which also might be useful as a basis for looking at needs in the health area.

Rod Griffiths
Should we be using resource allocation to drive policy objectives such as the shift to primary care and Health of the Nation targets, which are declared policy objectives? Or do we carry out the resource allocation process as a flat, objective exercise, and then load the policy objectives on top of that?

Rosemary Geller
If for example, we used the population numbers plus smoking prevalence to allocate resources, we would be saying very clearly that reducing smoking prevalence is the most important thing to do.

Jim Paris
Can we not use the SMR formula as a temporary measure until the time when the FHSA registers and associated morbidity data will give a more accurate reflection of identified need within each area or GP practice? Then aggregated

practice data would give identified need in certain policy areas and we can obviously choose those areas. Smoking could be one, coronary heart disease or hypertension could be others. The evidence from Scandinavia where they have already done this is that, for example, there isn't the undetected hypertension resulting in stroke as there is in this country. I would like to see the formula as a temporary measure until we have a much better way of assessing population needs based on more accurate data from general practice.

Andrew Harris

I think the answer to policy resourcing depends on how flexible the system can be. I don't see a problem in taking something like smoking prevalence, which is a perfectly good measure of a very major health need. The problem is whether you can find incentives for commissioning authorities to purchase the appropriate care to address that need. For example, each year a sum could be allocated to recognise performance change using the bench mark data that has come out recently from the centre.

Rod Griffiths

Several of the papers we have heard today have raised the issue of what is the resource allocation for? Is it in order to fund hospitals, in which case there is one set of assumptions you might make, or is it in order to make the population healthy, in which case there is a different set of assumptions. I am still left with this question unanswered. We know there is a good correlation between measures of health and deprivation, and we can give more money to those areas that seem to be using more, but what have we got to do to make people equally healthy? If it is equity of health we are looking for, I think we have still got a long way to go and I doubt that the formulae are going to help.

Resource Allocation & Health Needs
27th October 1993
Delegate List

Dr P R Alderson
Registrar in Public Health Medicine
Powys Health Authority

Ms Felicity Andrew
Chief Information Analyst
Coventry Health Authority

Dr Madhavi Bajekal
Research Fellow
Department of General Practice
St Mary's Hospital Medical School

Mr David Evans
Executive Officer
North East Thames Regional Health Authority

Mrs Ann Barton
Director of Commissioning
Lancashire Family Health Services Authority

Miss Deborah Baxter
Projects Officer
Yorkshire Regional Health Authority

Miss Cindy Billingham
Senior Analyst
West Midlands Regional Health Authority

Ms Anita Bird
Economic Adviser, Operational Research
NHS Management Executive

Mr Edward Bramley-Harker
Economic Assistant, Operational Research
NHS Management Executive

Mr Neil Brent
Finance Manager
Wessex Regional Health Authority

Dr P E Brooks
Director of Public Health and Planning
Herefordshire Health Authority

Mr Paul Brotherton
Assistant Director – Needs Assessment
New River Health Authority

Mr Ken Buckingham
Health Economist
Cornwall & Isles of Scilly Health Authority

Dr Robert Carr
Senior Registrar in Public Health Medicine
Cornwall & Isles of Scilly Health Authority

Mr Martin Cassidy
Policy and Research Manager
Derbyshire Family Health Services Authority

Dr H Chapel
Registrar in Public Health Medicine
Cornwall & Isles of Scilly Health Authority

Ms J Chen
Research Student
The Institute of Public & Environmental Health
The University of Birmingham

Dr K K Cheng
Senior Lecturer
Department of Public Health & Epidemiology
The University of Birmingham

Mrs Susan Cooper
Planning & Development Manager
Dudley Family Health Services Authority

Dr Rob F Cooper
Director of Public Health
Solihull Health Authority

Ms Carole Cummins
Epidemiologist
West Midlands Regional Health Authority

Miss Louisa Dallmeyer
Finance Trainee
Riverside Community Health Care

Dr Alwyn Davies
Registrar in Public Health Medicine
Dudley Health Authority

Dr Tim Davies
Senior Registrar in Public Health Medicine
Wessex Regional Health Authority

Mrs Christine Daws
Regional Financial Planning Manager
Oxford Regional Health Authority

Mr Keith Derbyshire
Economic Adviser, Operational Research
NHS Management Executive

Mr R Dewhurst
Director of Information Services
Mersey Regional Health Authority

Mr Peter Dick
Project Leader, Operational Research
NHS Management Executive

Mr J O'Donnell
Contract Accountant
Forth Valley Health Board

Mrs Anne Dray
Director of Finance
Rotherham Health Authority

Dr Paul Ewings
District Statistician
Somerset Health Authority

Mr Roger Fox
Senior Lecturer, Department of Social Sciences
University of Greenwich

Dr Rosemary J Geller
Director of Public Health
Shropshire Health Authority

Dr F Gillet
Corporate Analyst
Mersey Regional Health Authority

Dr Estelle Gilman
Research Epidemiologist
The Institute of Public and Environmental Health
The University of Birmingham

Dr M Gilthorpe
Research Fellow
The Institute of Public & Environmental Health
The University of Birmingham

Dr Brian Guttridge
Consultant in Public Health Medicine
Cornwall & Isles of Scilly Health Authority

Mr Paul Hampshire
Finance & Contracting Director
Barking & Havering Health Authority

Ms Karen Hancock
Economic Adviser
Scottish Office NHS Management Executive

Dr Ursula Harries
Senior Research Officer
Salford Health Authority

Dr Andrew Harris
Clinical Director
Lambeth Southwark & Lewisham Family Health Services Authority

Mr Stuart Harris
Epidemiologist, Public Health Department
North Birmingham Health Care Purchasing Consortium

Dr John Hayward
Medical Adviser
Camden & Islington Family Health Services Authority

Mr T C Hennell
Corporate Analyst
Mersey Regional Health Authority

Mrs Sheila Howells
Director of Corporate Planning
Croydon Health Authority

Mrs Catharine P Jarvis
Assistant Health Needs Assessor
Wolverhampton Public Health Department

Mrs D Johnson
Public Health Scientist
Warwickshire Health Authority

Ms Elizabeth Kendall
Economic Assistant, Operational Research
NHS Management Executive

Dr Christopher Kenny
Consultant in Public Health Medicine
South Derbyshire Health Authority

Mr Brian Ledsham
Computer and Information Manager
Hereford and Worcester Family Health Services Authority

Dr J W Lord
Principal Lecturer in Health Care Studies
Manchester Metropolitan University

Mrs Cynthia Lyons
Health Needs Assessor
East Sussex Health Authority

Ms Rhona MacDonald
Regional Director of Finance
South Western Regional Health Authority

Mr Bryan Machin
Resource Allocation Manager
Yorkshire Regional Health Authority

Dr Ian Mackenzie
Registrar in Public Health Medicine
Cornwall & Isles of Scilly Health Authority

Mr J Masters
Research Associate, Dept. of Public Health Medicine
Great Yarmouth & Waveney Health Authority

Ms Susan Matthews
Assistant Director of Finance
Gloucestershire Health

Dr Adrian Mercer
Head of Planning
Manchester Family Health Services Authority

Dr P C Milner
Director of Public Health
Rotherham Health Authority

Dr Julie Moseley
Scientific Officer
Cornwall & Isles of Scilly Health Authority

Dr Stephen Munday
Consultant in Public Health Medicine
North Birmingham Health Care Purchasing Consortium

Ms Caroline Murphy
Medical Geographer
North West Anglia Health Authority

Ms Julia Neville
Director of Planning
Devon Family Health Services Authority

Mrs Barbara Newns
Planning & Contracts Manager
Shropshire Health Authority

Mr P S Novak
Information Manager
Barnsley Family Health Services Authority

Mrs Pat Owen
Scientific Officer
Cornwall & Isles of Scilly Health Authority

Mr G V Page
Director of Finance
Thameside Family Health Services Authority

Dr Jim Paris
Medical Adviser
Coventry Family Health Services Authority

Miss Daryl Peter
Director of Finance
Lancashire Family Health Services Authority

Dr Ceri Phillips
Head of Research
Newport Business School

Mr James Piercy
Research Fellow
York Health Economics Consortium

Dr Chris Price
Director of Health Policy
Norfolk Family Health

Dr David M Rea
Senior Lecturer in Social Policy
University of Plymouth

Mr N Relph
Director of Finance and Contracting
Oxfordshire Health Authority

Dr A J Richardson
Consultant in Public Health Medicine
Worcester & District Health Authority

Ms Sarah Richardson
Prime Care Manager
Health Commission for Wiltshire & Bath

Professor J Richman
Department of Health Care Studies
Manchester Metropolitan University

Dr W N Ritchie
Consultant in Public Health Medicine
Powys Health Authority

Ms K Robinson
Research Associate
Great Yarmouth & Waveney Health Authority

Dr J Saunders
Research Fellow, Department of Social Sciences
University of Greenwich

Mr P Shobrook
Health Geographer
North Birmingham Health Care Purchasing Consortium

Ms Anita Sims
Public Health Information Officer
North Derbyshire Health Authority

Dr R T Sims
Consultant in Public Health Medicine
Canterbury & Thanet District Health Authority

Mr P Smith
Senior Lecturer in Economics
University of York

Dr Kevin Snee
Consultant in Public Health Medicine
North Derbyshire Health Authority

Dr Lillian Somervaille
Research Epidemiologist
The Institute of Public & Environmental Health
The University of Birmingham

Mr Ron Stamp
Manager, Research & Development
South West Thames Regional Health Authority

Mr Alan Stephens
Director of Finance
East Surrey Health Authority

Mrs Sumathi Sundram
Director of Finance
Suffolk Family Health Services Authority

Ms Julie Taylor
Research Fellow, Social Work Research Centre
University of Stirling

Dr Ken Taylor
Consultant Physician
West Birmingham Health Authority

Miss Andrea Thomas
Senior Analyst
West Midlands Regional Health Authority

Mrs Sarah F Thompson
Director of Contracting
Bedfordshire Health Authority

Mr Tom Travers
Director of Finance
Hereford & Worcester Family Health Services Authority

Dr Rosalea Watters
Director of Community Care/Medical Officer of Health
Eastern Health Board, Dublin

Mr N C Webb
Director of Finance
Walsall Health Authority

Mr Richard Wilson
Research Associate
The Institute of Public & Environmental Health
The University of Birmingham

Mrs C Woodfine
Primary Care Manager
Health Commission for Wiltshire & Bath

Mr David Yates
Head of Performance Monitoring
Oxford Regional Health Authority

Keynote Speakers

Dr Vera Carstairs
National Co-ordinator, Health Service Research Networks
University of Edinburgh

Professor Rod Griffiths
Director
The Institue of Public & Environmental Health
The University of Birmingham

Dr Bobbie Jacobson
Director of Public Health
East London & The City Health Authority

Professor Brian Jarman
Professor of Primary Health Care
St Mary's Hospital Medical School

Organisers

Mrs Elaine Greaves
Short Course Secretary
The Institue of Public & Environmental Health
The University of Birmingham

Mrs Carol Richards
Secretary
Department of Public Health & Epidemiology
The University of Birmingham

Dr Rachel Strachan
Short Course Organiser
The Institute of Public & Environmental Health
The University of Birmingham

Printed in the United Kingdom for HMSO
Dd297643 2/94 C15 G3396 10170